MIND HEALTH AND YOU

MIND HEALTH AND YOU

C.S VIKAS AGGARWAL
C.A GUNJAN GANGWAL

Foreword by

Mr. Rajender Mahajan

GenNext Publication

ISBN: 978-93-8022-353-7

First Published, 2019

Published by

GenNext Publication
5, Ansari Road
Daryaganj, New Delhi-110002
Phone: 9811692060
E-mail: gennextpublication@hotmail.com

Printed at: G. Print Process, Delhi.

Contents

Foreword

CS VIKAS AGARWAL is associated with us as a consultant in respect of E-commerce and Taxation related matter. I remember when he met my son, he had to face a lot of problems in life. He was very disappointed with the health problems and CS course studies. I induced him to turn on his life to achieve mental health and life satisfaction. Later, he gained more awareness and control over the emotions. He changed his whole mindset. Now, I am happy for him because he has written his next book on the topic of Mind and Physical health.

His book explains the concept of Mind Health and Body are connected. This book interprets how to achieve personal freedom in life by breaking the boundaries of Image creation. There are a lot of books are available in the market in respect of Mind and Health. The main exciting thing about the book is giving real-time practice so that the reader can know the real art of living, enjoy his rest of life in happiness, and know the delicious taste of success. It will guide the reader in all aspect of life.

It covers up the topics like Mind Conditioning, Body image, Religion, Emotions, Dance, Music, Aura, Planets, Non-Conflict management, eating habits, and nutritious diet for the body. The chapter of 'Health Eating habits for your child' discussing the Baby diet plan according to age. It can help the parents in taking necessary steps for a child to recover from trauma. The chapter of Nutrition's is encouraging for consumption of natural food intake for the balance of diet and weight management. It gives a lot of idea of selecting daily meal supported by the journey of the author.

The contents are always attention-grabbing, each time the reader will never feel either confused, bored, or just indifferent. In the sense of perspective and ideas, it gives the new wings to the reader that helps to fly as much as high possible. The views of quotes, the experience of the writer's life and other patterns of the writing of book are making more sense. Everyone will be happy to read all the contents of the book.

Mr. Rajender Mahajan

(Owner of the brand name
"Osaka" and "Sonia" in India)

Preface

This book is a memorable journey towards self-realization and light of truth. It is going to assist you in eliminating darkness of life and stress forever. It gives you room to listen to the inner sound and breathe deeply. It covers up the necessary eating habits and essential part of the nutritious diet for the body. It will guide you in all stages of life whether it is the art of becoming a conscious and bliss or in all affairs of business and professional world. Thus, you will be able to get rid of whatever you're suffering.

Acknowledgment

I would like to give special thanks to "Mrs. Sakshi Gupta" for advised and assisted me discovery of all topics discussed in this book. She inspired me for lot of research and setting high standards which formed the basis of this book.

I want to express my gratitude towards my parents, other family members, and professionals who give me freedom to explore.

I am grateful to my colleagues and friends especially Mr. J.S. Rawat, Mr. Naresh Jha, Ms. Anushri Bhattacharjee, Mr. Jatinder Hans, and Mr. Naveen for encouraging, suggestion, and helped me to complete this book.

Introduction

I was going through the tough time in my life. I was depressed due to my overweight problem and regular stress of studies of C.S. (Company Secretary) Course. The work pressure of my job and facing the severe issue of an accident case was the most significant threat of my life. I was going to die at 30.

You know what teaches you?

How to handle every situation logically.

It's challenging to find.

What do you want to do in your life?

What is the reason behind it?

However, I managed to meet with my life Coach "Mr. Rajender Mahajan" who told me that how can I enjoy my life during my rest of life?

He pushed me to keep moving forward in your life:

- ☞ 'The only person who can help you is the one you see in the mirror.'
- ☞ 'Believe in yourself and belief would make it true.'
- ☞ 'Think before, decide at least for one minute.'
- ☞ 'You cannot change the past life, but change your life today.'
- ☞ 'Start implementing small but good changes in your life and feel the difference.'
- ☞ 'Don't rely on anyone it's your life don't give chance other people to handle it.'

- ☞ 'Why do we try to stay in calm? Can we not live in peace too?'
- ☞ 'God blessed us unlimited mind powers, we second after the God.'
- ☞ 'If there is enough courage to pursue your life goals, then you can achieve almost anything, all your dreams will come true.'
- ☞ "It doesn't matter how slow you go until you stop."—Canfucius
- ☞ "Whatever you want is on the other side of fear." —Jack Canfield

I read this phrases, and it has proved to be true. I feel stressed at times. Later on, I realize depression and happiness are two aspects of the same coin. You don't feel misery in your life; then you sense nothing in your life. Emotions are thoughts about you as what is happening around you. If you have no emotions, you have no opinion about life. You learn the taste of defeat; then you can enjoy the delicious taste of success. When I came to know the truth of life; I am incredibly grateful for those people, who had become a reason for depression in my life. In this way, I do not consider them in any way as unimportant because they are people who brought me here. I have tried to explain those things in this book to that I had learned over the years.

So, you are ready for enlightenment...

Chapter - 1

Mind conditioning and emotional health

Mind Conditioning and Practice Technique

The universe is a fertile land. Your dreams, thoughts, mind perception, emotions are roots, seeds, and magnet. Let's learn how to throw seeds in the universe, attract everything, and get success in your life.

We are linked to the subconscious mind. We can practice technique and condition our mind by acceptance of concepts,

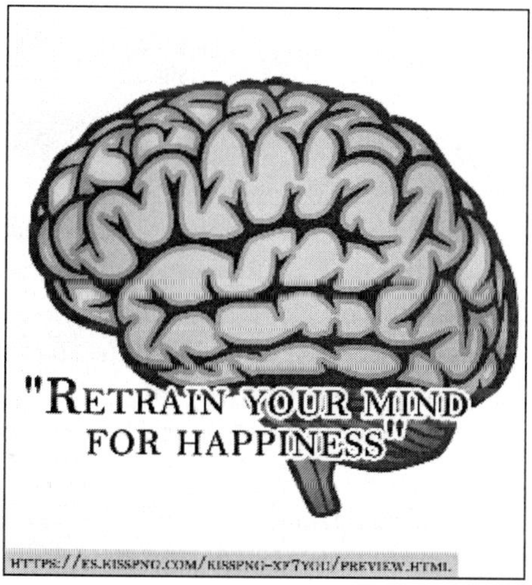

Fig 1.

positively oriented thoughts, trust, and confidence through which we can become rich, happy, successful, and healthy.

Your mind is the only and the ultimate key to all your achievements. We can have positive thinking and beliefs can change the habits, nature, personality, and everything around us. We can condition or control our subconscious mind to perform wonders, achieve the impossible in studies, career, business, and relationship. It can make fulfill our dreams and desires.

Like an excellent horticulturist, based on the habit of thinking you put the seeds of thoughts in your subconscious mind. It takes some time to accept your subconscious mind. It does not make any difference between seeds of any kind, even if it is good or bad. As soon as you transplant in your subconscious mind, it will grow in your body and environment. Begin now to sow the thoughts of peace, happiness, love, sympathy, faith. Accept them entirely in your conscious logical mind. Keep sowing to plant these beautiful seeds of thoughts in mind, and you will reap a great harvest. Every thought is a reason, and each condition has its own influence. So, it is essential that you take charge of your thoughts.

In which state all mental suffering ends, is called Nirvana. Nirvana is an un-ended state of great joy and peace. *I am going to burn a candle of Bliss. To detach you from griefs and sufferings, a flame of bliss is put out for pure happiness. I will try to condition the mind throughout the chapters through putting good quotes of Bliss, happiness, fun, and peaceful life which shows the spiritual voice of authenticity.*

'I'm enjoying my re-programming brain successfully.'

> "Your unhappiness arises not from the circumstances of your life, but from the conditioning of your mind." –- Eckhart Tolle

Happiness quotes make your happiness is a habit

Language is not created by God. God understand pictures based visualizations. If we constantly repeat the same series of words, then the mind starts thinking from inside, and it will begin to convert into the pictures, which can reach to God easily. In this universe, every living-being can send the requests to God in the form of imagination or visualization, which provides the opportunity to be united with the Lord. It allows you to craft your reality and it is quite simple – to chant, to harmonize voice, to sing, or to connect with all of these. Neither great skill nor brave effort is required for this.

So, I keep these hilarious and happy quotes after the end of headings or paragraph or chapter, keeping in mind the specific reason. It will help you to sow the seeds of good habits and sticking to them will support you to improve your work-life balance. You can enjoy after every moment of life, whether it is sufferings or facing any difficulties in life. You can quickly come out of it by enjoying it.

External interventions may influence your thoughts. But, you can control your thoughts, depending on how you react to your environment. You think them comfortably, it seems like you have no control over your thoughts. But, this is not correct. Positive and negative thoughts cannot exist in our mind simultaneously. Both can cancel one another out. The positive emotions like love, compassion, social support, and job satisfaction, etc., improve individual physical health and psychological well-being. By focusing on the positive emotions of trust, delight, joy, love, calm, etc., one can avoid the negative emotions of sadness, hatred, anxiety, hostile, revenge, greediness, superstition, anger, etc. By disciplining the mind to only approving positive emotions ahead, so that negative emotions are not permitted to enter it.

You have to live more consciously in present moments and have to connect all activities, situations, and events of life by saying "Happy / Enjoy / Love / Thanks / Like" to enjoy whatever you do. For example, you are walking on the road; you have to imagine that "Thank you, God in the form of your blessing, I'm enjoying wonderful weather on this road." But do not hurry and think while reacting to any situation

Fig 1.1

or decision. You must react positively, in any situation. In this way, you have to open the new wings of your imagination. To create such a kind of association with daily life activities, you have to practice continuously as much as possible. After that, you will be able to 'see' new twists to your thoughts and concepts in your mind. Let's try this with another example. Whenever you eat your food the next time, you can say it "Yummy, Yummy! I love the taste of Juicy fruits." Even, in the case of negative circumstances like Road Rage, Workplace Conflicts, Break up with Friends, Failure in exams or any other situation, you should stay connected with positive thoughts. You cannot do so much, then you can say after the completion of the work or after any activity, say "Maja Aa Gaya" or "it was fun" or "very much enjoyed." When you practice it every day, you will be able to realize that it has become a habit. You will be amazed to see the huge changes coming in your daily life. The energy flows in a

Fig 1.2

positive direction, wherever you want to move it, it will direct. After some time you will realize, how the toughest roads of life become a beautiful destination. That is where my plea for change in our education set up for the new generation.

Our traditional concepts of 'Satsang' or 'Spiritual Workshop' is an essential step in religious and spiritual practice through which anyone may come across new life concepts and learning. Satsang is an opportunity to serve God, love for others, and provide holistic answers. When we regularly participate in the Satsang or Spiritual workshops, some followers get answered of questions what they have in their mind. Even, they usually get positive energies, embracing truth, and divine consciousness.

'I love increasingly disillusioned positive outlook.'

"There is a powerful way to attract those things in the brain that will be good together with it."

Our Body can function perfectly till last breath of the life.

A human body is created to function perfectly till the last breath and minute of the life. Health, balance, perfection, healing, regeneration, and survival are laws of the body.

Instead of focusing more on the treatment of illness, treatment of ignorance is to be done. Illness is byproduct our strange habits. Know the secrets of ultimate truth, health, nutrition, root causes of diseases, and eliminate the root causes. Well-being can be achieved through normal and healthy habits. Remove the word 'Sickness' from your life.

> 'I am very happy that I measure deeply adjusted health.'

Impact of emotions on health

Your body responds to your thoughts and actions. When you are stressed, or upset, our body giving a signal that body is out of balance or something that's not correct. Hostility, anger, frustration, sadness, tears, disappointments are the highest scorer when it comes to negative emotions.

Negative thoughts encourage all kinds of illnesses.

Fig 1.3

For example, you can face issues related to hypertension or dyspepsia after a, particularly stressful event. Health issues due to depression may cause:

- Less energy for doing work and increase tiredness;
- Less or more sleeping problem;
- Unexpected weight gain or loss;
- Week concentration, no clear decisions making;
- Irritation and feeling of restlessness;
- Feelings of suicide and hopelessness.

A Body can be out of balance due to emotions. The emotions maybe the reason for the body out of balance can cause the issues like:

- Constipation,
- Appetite and stomach issues,
- Back Pain and Regular Pain in a chest,
- Dry Mouth, Tiredness, and Sweating,
- High Blood pressure and Trouble in Sleeping,
- Stiff neck, High weight gain or loss, weak immunity.

I struggled many years when I was attending my school or was appearing for Company Secretary Exams. I had undergone a high level of stress. Sometimes, while participating in the examination, I had to face severe headaches and anxiety disorders. Every time, I tried to achieve that level of perfection, failed every time to overcome the situation of emotional distress. It would have been easy if I had been brought in that environment from the beginning. I used to avoid junk food. I started work on to taking care of myself. I started to sleep properly at the time of exam which enough to give proper energy and fresh mood.

Instead of convincing myself that I shall be failed in exams, I used to go examination room with positive thoughts "I have passed my examination with good marks." I was beginning to believe that "I have received good marks in exams." Only one exam is not enough for my carrier. I can have a better opportunity in the future too. I avoided worse thing which leads to creating a bad scenario.

So, I stressed out over exams and whole-body allows for balance and harmony to return.

> 'I love myself, not an emotional gangster. '

How to improve emotional health

In some ways, we can improve our emotional health. Firstly, identify your feelings and think why they arise. If we get success in getting the reason behind disappointments, stress, and miseries in our life then indeed we are now prepared to take the necessary steps to overcome this situation. Please check the following ways:-

Take measures to prevent stress

You can feel stress at times. How you react to stress, it will determine its effect on you. Whether you can manage it or not, take steps to stop stress.

You may express your feelings to a professional person

When stress, disappointment, anxiety are the cause of physical health issues. If you keep this feeling inside, then it gets worse as a result. It is possible that your family member or any friend could not help you better in this. At this time, we can take the assistance of a psychologist, a spiritual advisor, and any other specialized person who can improve your emotional health.

Better to be focused on the positive side

It's better to concentrate on the positive sides avoid negative feelings. It's not necessary to deal with negative emotions; we can make way for positive things in our life. You can write down the negative thoughts on a paper, after which the brain will not repeatedly heart he alarm. "To restore balance, we have to develop positive vision here for you to take positive action" - Dalai Lama. It's proved from the latest studies and researches that having a positive outlook can improve your quality of life.

Build up resilience

It is better to understand about flexibility and ability to recover from any issues. If we have to face any problem, then its solution is hidden in that problem too. It will enable the ability to handle stress appropriately.

Resilience may deal the issues with different approaches, make the things in a perspective way, create a sense of confidence, and if any problem comes then, it can provide all the capabilities to solve issues.

Care yourself and develop better habits

If we want to enjoy good emotional health, it is necessary for me to choose a healthy diet, sleep well, and do regular exercises. Please avoid using drugs, alcoholic drinks, and any other things on a regular basis which can cause health problems.

Peace of mind and body

We can check out some way by which we can calm our mind like watching religious TV channels, meditation, listening to music, doing yoga, and learning Reiki are some manners to bring our emotions into control. The best of them is meditation. It keeps your mind free of unnecessary self-talk or compulsive thinking. However, people avoid this quickly because when they are willing to do so, the brain starts taking other needless instructions from somewhere else without your permission. Now, we are not awake to inner spirituality, in a minute we cannot achieve it. If, we practice regularly in daily routine and then you can easily pay attention to where the inconsistency is. Initially do it for at least 15 minutes every day. The primary method of watching light entering into your body, concentrate on breathing, and list of yoga poses, etc. improves your concentration. So, you can become fit, flexible, and energetic. It relaxes your body in a few minutes. You can increase this daily interval of time. If you follow the method of meditation in your daily life, it can easily overcome the issues of depression, anxiety, and sadness. It increases intelligence, inner peace, memory, and creativity.

> "Emotional self-control is result of hard work, not an inherent skill." – Travis Bradberry.

Check the practice below:

Please check the True or false for the following.

Q I - I would always ask myself, what should I do or not?

Q II - It is difficult to forget and apologize for me.

Q III - The Glass of water is mine, always half-Empty, not every time half full

Q IV - I criticize about myself.

Q V - What do I feel about myself in thinking people.

Q VI - I feel my mistakes and succeed in finishing them.

Q VII - I mainly make a special effort to please others.

Q VIII - I think the weight of the world on my shoulders.

Q IX - Failure is partially worse than an overall failure.

Q X - I always tell those who care about me.

Q XI - I'm not sure that I did a good job until someone else points out.

Q XII - I always ask for forgiveness for the mistake.

Q XIII - If I could not perform like others, then it does not mean that I am not like them.

Q XIV - If I cannot do anything well, then there is nothing to do with it.

Check your Results

Provide one point to yourself every question you answered with a "TRUE."

- 0 - 4

  You have a positive outlook, and the feeling of love in your heart is intense.

- 5 - 8

  Due to the negative thoughts coming to mind, struggling with negative emotions.

- 9 or more

  You are afraid of criticism about yourself. Overcoming the sense of doubt or inferiority towards yourself is necessary.

> "Until you realize how easily it is for your mind to be manipulated, you remain the puppet of someone else's game." -- Evita Ochel

> 'I enjoying conditioned to believe things because it easy way to create a calm mind.'

Chapter - 2

Body image and Facts about Human Brain

What Is Image?

An Image is a visual picture or external appearance of any person through which we can easily recognize him. Just like a photographic image or statue or painting showing a portrait or an impression of any person.

Type of Image

Inner Image and Body Image

Body Image

Body-image also refers to what we think, feels about ourselves and how we react to our self-reported physical attributes. It is connected to your thoughts like what you think about your body weight, shape, and skin color. Body Image developed through several mediums like TV, Magazines, Friends, Parents, Relatives, and Audiences.

An important thing about the positive body image is the person who readies to accept, regard and recognize his body. It improves the self esteem and effect outlook of society. It becomes easy to live with a stable lifestyle with healthy attitudes and belief system. All habits relating to food and exercise shall be adapted according to the needs of your body.

'I am beautiful for the image of my body.'

Inner Image

Every person either intentionally or unintentionally generates an image of a particular identity or personality of himself. The Inner image is the own view, and it is nothing to do or relationship with the outer world. Inner-image is the result of grasp and experience, what we think and observe about ourselves.

Since childhood, I always wondered "Who am I'm?" It is really I am or someone else. Every time after a few years there is always a question arises in front of me that I really don't know anything in the world. I still remember the experience, I was sitting in my classroom, and I was starring outside the class thinking about me. Suddenly, my teacher came and stood for five to ten minutes to derive my attention. He tried to get replies from me. But, I was not able to pay attention to my teacher or maybe I was lost somewhere else. The atmosphere around me was joyful and which was better than the outside world. I was experiencing inner peace, instead of miseries and sadness. The teacher was angry and shouted unusually "Maybe you are an insect or devil who must be killed at once." She again confused me about my personality. At this time, if I pursue outside world which was unpleasant and stressful.

> 'I'm enjoying inner happiness.'
> "Never see your happiness in others it will make you feel alone but search it in yourself. You will feel happy." -- Jelly

Breaking the boundaries of Image Creation and achieve personal freedom.

A person was crossing an elephant. He immediately stopped, puzzled about the fact how the big animal like Elephant was organized only by a small rope made from their front legs. There were no iron chains and no lockup cages. It was clear that elephants could have been separated from their bonds at any time, there was some reason behind this which was not allowed the Elephant to do. He looked at a trainer and asked him why the elephant stood there and did not make any effort to go away. The trainer said that "when the elephant was very small, we used a similarly shaped rope to tie it and in that age, it was enough to stop the elephant, as it grows up, the elephant always believes that it will not succeed in avoiding this rope.

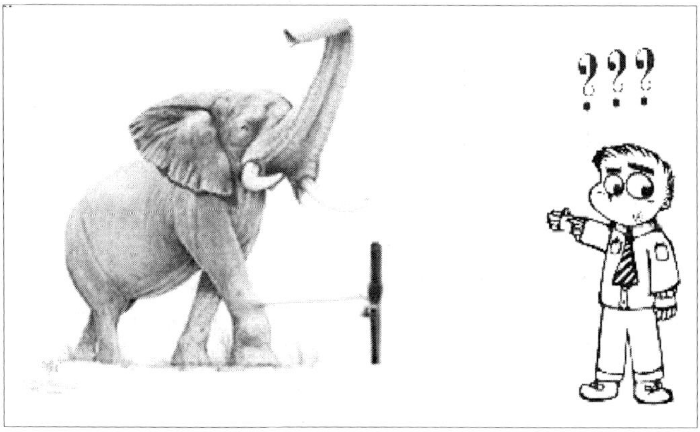

Fig 2.0

Therefore, elephant believes that the rope can still catch it, so it never tries to be free." The person was shocked that this animal can be free from their bonds at any time because this animal believed that he could not do it, they were right where they were. Just like the elephants, many of us are hanging on a belief system that we cannot do anything because we had failed before?

Through every person, either intentionally or unconsciously, which we call life, through its process, a particular image creates a specific personality of itself. You have created this image within yourself, nothing to do with reality. It is one specific image that you have made, mostly unconsciously. Many people have created a conscious image of themselves. All others have made the images according to any pattern or external conditions. In the modern era, enhancing the quality of our lives has become one of our main aims. In this endeavor, we insist on enhancing the daily affairs of life concerning our work, business, and family. Despite all the efforts, there is often lack of joy and happiness in our personal or professional life. If you create a new self-image, the way you want to be. If you know enough and can recreate your image, utterly new image, whatever you want. You should be ready to leave the old image, and instead of acting unconscious, you work consciously. You can form an image that provides you the maximum support, an image that will create a lot of happiness around you. It must be portable, you can carry it easily, wherever you go. You can create an image that is the closest to your inner nature. But, I never recommend you to generate self-image for you which consist of ego. You have to raise your perception and recognize yourself. Even, you can see the inner nature is peaceful, free of ego, not impressive but too stable and robust. You have to become conscious and bliss. If you know you are something from your previous image, then in such a way it will not be possible. See that there is more love in the new image, what we are creating now is better than what we have earlier. You are that form (shadow) of auspicious divinity. You have to become an observer or evidence of thoughts that usually flow currently from our mind.

I used to travel by train to several cities in India. Whenever the train passed through the village and rivers, I found myself as that I was sitting at the side of the river and observing that the river was flowing. I never felt that I'm floating with the stream and ultimately all the water of the river flows into seas. Take another example; from childhood, I usually look towards the sky. I wished that I could be a part of the sky like a bird and a cloud. I also wanted to fly, and this was not possible. If I was not a river or a bird, how can I make myself as part of my thoughts? If someone called me Saint or Joker or something else, then I do not start to create the images for me. I have just become a witness of thoughts. **We can achieve personal freedom in this way.**

> 'I am very happy that I have achieved my personal freedom.'

Amazing Facts about Human Brain

There are several facts about the human brain. In the areas of science, the studies of the human brain are continued to update, and the scientists believe that they do not know much about the brain. Here are a few fascinating facts about the human brain.

Fig 2.1

(i) The weight of our brain is near about 3 pounds. 60% of the dry weight is fat, by which the brain is the fattiest part of the body.

(ii) The brain consists of almost two percent of the total weight of the body, uses twenty percent of total energy and oxygen intake.

(iii) Our brain is Seventy-two percent water. There is only two percent dehydration to affect our memory, attention, and other perceptional skills.

(iv) 25% of the body's cholesterol stays in the brain. Brain cells die when there is not enough cholesterol.

(v) Our brain requires an ongoing supply of oxygen. Even 5 minutes without oxygen can cause many brain cells to die or tend to severe brain damage.

(vi) Brain information goes up 268 miles per hour. It's impressive and fast.

(vii) Our brain produces roughly twelve to twenty-five watts of electricity. It is the reason that the brain is called a "random thought generator." So, the average brain generates nearly Fifty thousand thoughts per day.

(viii) In every minute, 750 - 1,000 ml of blood flow through the brain. It is quite enough to fill a bottle of wine.

'I like to learn and train about the human brain.'

Some facts about human memory

The memory means collecting information about previous events in our brain. If you know the nature of memory, then it affects our brains, emotions and our whole body. In this world, every human being is consists of five basic elements (Water, Air, Fire, Earth, and Space) in a balanced way. These all the five elements working within our body begin immediately after the work of that memory. The whole approach of seeing life depends on two eyes that mainly loaded with memory. When you watch at a bunch of people, among these several people, you know one face that you are already familiar with; you will see that face is more clearly visible than others. We are more concern about a face as we can easily remember faces as compared to names connected with that face. Your eye always connected to memory that is how you identify people. Otherwise, it cannot be possible. If memories result from a combination of abilities such as studying theories, which are difficult to remember in comparison with the identity of realities. For instance, students or any other person, still have to keep the points to remember that what he had learned today during the day. Let's check out another example of your tongue. If you are born in India and your tongue is filled with the taste of vegetarian food. If you travel to another country, where a vegetarian diet is not available, you feel that it does not taste good because your tongue is fully loaded with memory. It wants the same things again; otherwise, it will suffer.

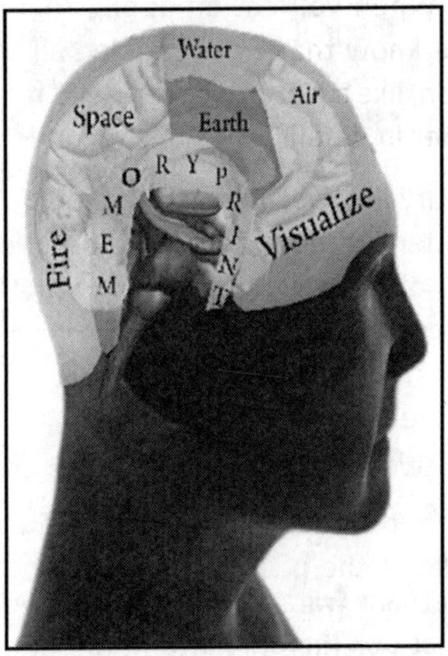

Fig 2.2

Your whole body is just a body of memory. Perhaps, you miss your ancestors or not. But, you are not aware of the fact that his nose is sitting on your face. Your whole body closely resembles your parents. Your body always remembers your ancestors, even if you forget your parents. There is an in-house program, DNA never forgets. It does not allow you to see what's going on inside in any way. We are some fantastic examples of resemblance across generations. The memory is not just what you get from the outside world, and each cell has its memory in the body. When you eat an apple, then it becomes you. From childhood, we know that we are taking all the major decisions by visual perception, like a picture we can get it from our memory and check it for further in detail.

Most of us hold a photo memory archive, in which the majority of people's memory for visual content is more detailed than other types of content. It is the process of what we see; memory prints itself on all levels to the primary level. That is why we are referring to an absolute reality which comprises action and memory. Every past action exists in the form of memory. Our present moment is wholly based on our whole past.

Further, you can understand that in the present moment your entire future is also included because the past is changing as you have done. It is prefabricating you, and the future that is going to happen will be the same as you are currently living in. In this manner, memory has a significant influence on our future and present life.

Our memory is wonderful, pyrotechnics, and incredible. Although, it is fully mechanical.

> 'I am loving the memory of joy in the present suffering.'

Chapter - 3

Religion, Spirituality, & Entrepreneurship

Religion

We can live a life as a Hindu or Christian or Muslim mind. But, our Soul cannot follow or belong to any religion. Minds may be different as we have many cultures, refinements, community, societies, and religions. Each community or different cultures develop a different mentality. A Mind is a social origination or derivation.

Religion means to guide peoples in the form of setting up mindsets, rules, faith, and beliefs of followers. All religions guide the human brotherhood. Everyone in this world has an authority to reach the Lord. If we are saying that my religion is the only authentic religion, which means it is not logical. Every person can reach the Lord. The several paths are going towards God. We have to select the one, leave others. We can select only one at a time. Like you cannot drive the two cars at a time. We have to pick one way to reach infinity.

My parents are living a simple life in which they used to follow every day the traditional practices of their Religion like reading of holy books and chanting words or mantras. They usually spend their time on prayers of God, watching religious channels on Television, and meeting the family's 'Gurus' who teaches - how we can live a peaceful life and choose a path through which we can reach to God by keeping our faith on the God. Because of their trust in God, they have their belief system and rules for their life through which they have a positive feeling, a better immunity system, and a lot of energy for a daily lifestyle.

Benefits of adopting a religion

If you regularly participate in religious services, it can help you -

- To get encouragement in their happiness and to incorporate a healthy lifestyle in daily routines.
- You feel more joy and peace.
- Work against anxiety and stress.
- Getting the same benefits of meditation like
  - Increase the concentration and defense power,
  - Keeps the blood pressure low, slow aging, etc.
- Prayer may assist us in feeling more closed to God.

Apparently, followers of religion never choose regular habits of drinking alcohol and smoking. They liked to live a healthy life overall.

> 'I love all religion as essence of all religion are same.'

Spiritual Practice

Spiritual means faith, truth, and belief system that connects with the consciousness or spirit. Spirituality is examining or knowing about our inner-self. It's a kind of journey of awakening about our inner identity and its discovery of self. If, we considered an average life of a human being is full of stress. They spend maximum time in his official work, moving in traffic, and other daily routine tasks. An ordinary person has less time to spend on his family and self-awareness.

It is correct to say that we do not know our inner self. If I see my life, I was studying in school days; there was always questions in my mind about myself. I wanted to discover myself. But, my teachers and elders had suggested me that this will not help you a lot, it would be better to live a normal life and enjoy it. Even, no teachers in the school and colleges who can teach about inner engineering. They were not interested in giving proper guidance about 'who you are,' 'why you are on this earth,' and 'how you can achieve true happiness.' Everyone in the school and colleges wanted to focus on the work that was instructed to follow. There was no scope of self-analyzing, or any self-awakening process was going on. They were used to say that "It's not your right age to think about it, focus on your studies and plan for the future for your career development and goals."

In fact, we are living in a world where the sharp intelligence of human being is destroying everything, press manipulating information, university exploiting knowledge, religion is not encouraging morals, and the doctor is spoiling the health. Everyone has their view or understanding to look into the things. People listen as much as they want to hear. I think our life is a big mystery which needs to be resolved. We have to make our own life ourselves. People who always rely on destiny and lead to a life where they wait for things will happen. Things will never be going to happen automatically. There is a not a rocket science behind this. We have to create our efforts for everything has to happen.

We look into the life of The Great spiritual master 'The Buddha.' He was born in a village nearby small town of Kapilavastu situated in Nepal. His father was King Suddhodana. When he was sixteen years old, he was married to a beautiful princess, Yashodhara. The king

Fig 3.0

gifted them three palaces according to the seasons and provided them all the comforts and luxuries of the life. They took pleasure in their days and never considered the life which is outside his premises.

Soon, he became frustrated and disillusioned with the liveliness of the pleasure dome, and he was supposed to come out from it. Eventually, he left his kingdom and beloved persons behind his monk life of wandering soul. He started his discovery of the truth, he went to the several places and met with sharp and intelligent masters of his time. He never achieved the right level of satisfaction. He did not end his journey and continued his research for himself. Few years of severe penance and frugality gave him knowledge of his self-enlightenment. His diet consisted of only fruits and leaves. He spent his maximum time in sitting meditation. Sometimes, he did not eat anything and faced more difficulties in life than anyone else.

He concluded that from his both life of, luxury in the palace, and difficult life forest which is a way of freedom. There is no happiness in overdoing the things. He started eating again and recover his strength once again.

After that his struggle ended, he felt the causes of his agony and sufferings, tried to find all the solution for it. He attained the highest wiseness and understood them as he was in real moments of enlightenment. It was the moment that he was the first time unconditional, sensible, truly free person.

His endeavored to bring up the bliss in the life, not pleasure. Pleasure is not real happiness; it depends on the misery. Bliss is excellence; one walks beyond the duality of being pleasure and sorrow.

He never became furious or agitated or was not even spoken raspingly to anyone who was contrary to him. The life of the Buddha's as an example of the discovery of inner self and his path towards the self-awakening can achieve by anyone can become The Buddha. Although he left this world, the spirit of his kindness and compassion remain in us.

'I am happy to embrace spiritual practices.'

Entrepreneurship and Religion

I think entrepreneurship should emerge as religious influence on the lives of people. If I consider business as a religion, it is an organized collection of shared value or belief system that relate humanity to spirituality and moral values. I believe that there is an instant connection with the entrepreneur just like a soul mate. When I speak to an entrepreneur, I always feel that I have already met him before and we are the only soul on a shared journey. An entrepreneur world gives me a sense of peace. I feel a deep love and strong connection all the time. Just like a religious community, when someone needs help, enough people around him to help.

I believe an entrepreneur is also a real saint. They are hard-working and compassionate. Once upon a time, when I was sitting with an entrepreneur, suddenly the discussion was moved towards truthiness. He asked me what the difference between truthiness and falsehood is. As I said earlier, God has not invented the language. It was only developed by humans, and the whole humanity uses different languages for its advantages and disadvantages. According to General view, in which both the consent comes and the evidence proves that it is true. I think I do not know that they face how many difficulties in their business world and by speaking so many truths and lies they make the lives of millions of people. If a person is lying and is saving people's lives, then this lie will be better than the truth.

Fig 3.1

The real scenario is that in this world, it is difficult to survive in business if a business person tells all things as it is. It doesn't mean that I'm justifying the unfair practices of business. I think everybody should realize their responsibilities in the business world then everything will be okay automatically.

Cultural of entrepreneurship is a powerful, and attempts of entrepreneurship always influence people's lives compared to any other person. An employee has to follow the standard instructions of the enterprises as per the requirement of the entrepreneur. I have seen some employees don't want to understand the working culture of enterprises. Their target is to enjoy life in the office environment. They keep on wasting their time, indulging in activities like gossips, build a personal relationship, access social media like Facebook, WhatsApp, Twitter, Instagram, etc. They should understand that the company pays salaries to do work in the office, not for entertainment. Two short breaks and time of lunch are appropriate for them to rejuvenate again. I think all employees should pay more attention to the business growth of companies. They can create a profound difference in the figures and norms of the corporate world. They should add themselves to the Company's objective. According to the company's development, the growth of their careers is also linked to it.

I meet several entrepreneurs like accessory manufacturers, publishers, and other business enterprises in my daily life. One of the real entrepreneurs 'Mr. Saurabh Mahajan' hold up the 'Osaka' brand name in India (Director of PTIPL) involve in manufacturing camera accessories, provide genuine products and best services to customers. "Mr. Saurabh Gupta" (Director of LPPL) is one of the publishing company's pillars, always ensures proper discipline in the office. I learn beliefs and values from these enterprises:

- Everyone should get a job,
- An entrepreneur always tries to continue his business until his company can fulfill its salary obligation and other relevant expenses without any profit.
- They simply say focus on work. Find happiness and pleasure in the current working style.
- Do whatever, be different. If you feel that you are different from others, you will remain standing forever.

'I always enjoy my life journey with entrepreneurs.'

Religion and Spirituality Affect Our Health

Spirituality and Religious ideas can be rational as a part of human natural intelligence and competency. The study of Religion and spirituality, mainly focus on recognizing their primary fundamentals. They are primarily explanatory and depictive. According to researches on religion and spiritual practices, there are always favorable health outcomes. It is our belief systems in which religiosity and spiritualism is a key curriculum in the convergence of physical and natural powers. It explains how both work. It catches our health in two perspectives, emotions and behavior. Religiosity and spirituality jointly develop a better and healthier human in body, mind, and consciousness.

Religion assumes that we can change the course of existence by praying of God and chanting the mantras or words. Spirituality defines the ways to manage feelings inward, handle the occurrences, and manifestation of emotions.

Religion assists its disciples to examine their sentiments, more attempts to deal with the stress of mind with a positive attitude and lead to high morale.

Spirituality and religion will never be considered within the boundaries. Without spiritual power or religion practices, no one can become a noble person.

'My Religion – We are all peaceful and happy.'

Chapter - 4

Non Conflict Management and Resilience

Conflict is a situation of the discrepancy of viewpoint or opinion. The battle that occurs when two people do not provide any consent with any topic. The problems are straightforward, and the participants may observe the issues.

Reasons for conflicts

- Blaming others for past mistakes.
- Jealousy - you are encompassing emotion like insecurity and fear of lack of possessions.
- You are not happy with the work assigned to you. E.g., unorganized approach to the job, or more sensitive to own work.
- Contradiction or Unhealthy discussions - One person thinks that it should be done in any other way. Others do not agree with this.
- Dressing Etiquette - Improper dress for work. It can be unprofessional or too revealing.

Deal with Non-conflict management

The approaches to deal with conflicts:

- Focus on only work and do not make any personal relationships.

- Use organized strategies like identify, analyze, define, and evaluate.
- Listen carefully and take decisions after considering facts, instead of feelings.
- Take a bit of advice from people who have experience in life.
- Compromise if appropriate.
- Wait and take time to make decisions, do not hasten the resolution.

Have a quick look at the following dialogues of senior citizens:

Taco: I'm 84, my body is full of aches and pains.

Paco: Well, I'm 85, feel like a newborn baby.

Taco: Really.

Paco: Yep. No teeth, no hair, and I just wet my pants.

One or both parties do not feel that they are not personally attacked. This feeling of not being attacked is emotionally charged to both the situation of the participants. Conflict depends on person thinking; someone can make their destiny. According to them, their belief system can attract worse or good. If you are fighting for your desires, then life causes pain and conflict.

> 'I have all the capabilities and love to handle conflict with peaceful means.'

How to handle conflict at workplace

A Paradox in the workplace is indispensable. In the first stage, you should guide the employees to settle the dispute; it does not reach the over bloated status.

Conflict is a real facet of human engagement. Early or later, we all face a headache in the workplace. As the struggle in the workplace becomes an issue, if output and morale of office worker are both in a clash. It is necessary that managers and leadsman settle

Fig 4.0

this issue immediately. At that time, they require to addressing conflict solution strategy.

Conflicts and emotions are related to each other - fury, rage, irritation, frustration, and stubbornness are a waste of time. They usually disappeared after sometime. In this way, it needs to settle rapidly. By which the employees can return to work quickly and further focus on their work. I spent considerable time in handling conflicts among employees in companies. I should have acquired a master degree in psychology, instead of a degree in law. I have tried various ways to solve disputes between employees over the years. Sometimes, I found that employees do intentionally, or they were fighting for their rights.

In some cases, I was involved in the situation entirely or came after when a particular time of dispute had been passed. Every time I had to consider the best interests of the company. To keep the full decision in favor of the company, there was often a mental injury to anyone. I still remember the dispute when the two employees were shouting for the chair; I tried to stop them, as they were completely wasting their time and other's time. They were attracting the attention of other employees and were troubling them. I tried to convince them with every possible position. They were not ready because the reason was being that they lost their senses in misperceptions about another person's intentions, escalated negativity in their mind, overall the situation was out of control. Later,

I decided that if they do not want to stop the fight, they want to remain in the same position. Then they have to stay outside the company. After this, our company made the rule that no one will be allowed to speak against each other. If they have any problem against each other then they have to escalate it to their seniors; otherwise, the fine will be imposed on both.

Now, I am leaving the empty space in the boxes. So, you can start your own practice accordingly.

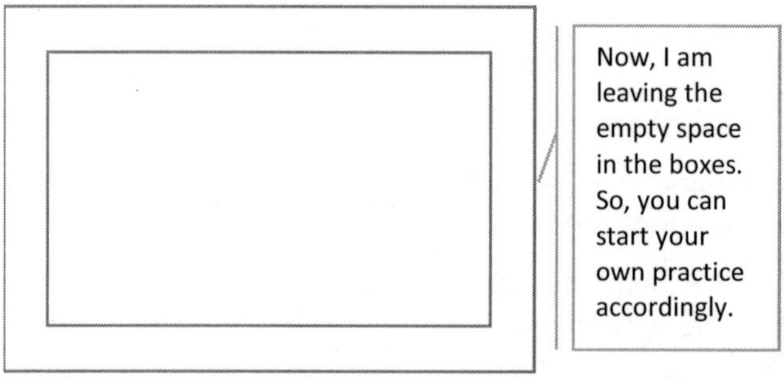

Ego Conflict management

A person should not speak my country, my caste, my religion, this kind of language. And by becoming silent, it should be realized so much that I have nothing.

What land is "mine"? What country is "mine"? This is our flag is higher than others; it works for children, it is for small children, these are childish things, we all hold the same. What difference created if my account, my scripture, my texts, my idol, my religion, my money.

Then came back to "mine," should be "mine."

And blinds are blinding, everyone crying.

They fall into well; they fall into wells every day. But their own well, why not fall?

My well will fall. You fall in your well; we will fall into our well!

There are small circles and borders; there are small limitations. I think all types of conflicts due to a misunderstanding of ego. Success and failure, Love and Hatred, Pleasure and miseries due to the ego. Why there is ego behind every conflict. Don't take it as personally and don't involve yourself.

An old man was living in the village with his cock. The cock started sounding "Kukuru Ku" every morning and sun was turned out. He was in the mistake that sun rises because of his cock. One day he was feeling furious and gave the last warning to villagers that he will leave the village and will go somewhere else. But villagers are not convinced with him. He left home and shifted to another village where cock again banged "Kukuru Ku" and sun turns out. He was laughing at the villagers, and they will realize the importance of the presence of mine. The message we get from this little story; he was a superstitious person. He believed that sun is limited with the boundaries of cock sounding. In this way, God's existence is not dependent on us. A man, who is free from the ego, gets the self-awakening like the Moon becomes cool and pure, always he becomes self-light and blissful.

Richard Gere: "None of us are getting out of here alive, so please stop treating yourself like an afterthought. Eat delicious food. Walk in the sunshine. Jump in the ocean. Tell the truth that you're carrying in your heart like a hidden treasure. Be silly, be kind, and be wired. There's no time for anything else."

Tuning of brain and heart for non-confliction management

The situation of the human mind is just like the spinning bees around their hive which are teased by anyone. The whispering thoughts like flies surround the human mind. A man confined by these thoughts lives in miseries and sorrow.

The human mind is being converted like an ill wound. It is not at its normal axis; it turned into an ulcer. All our attentiveness focused around our brain. Probably, you are all attention beginning to think about the organ, where it's got infected or sick wound. If we feel pain in the shoulders or in any other part of our body, then the brain indicates the pain around the same part of the body. But, there is no pain in the specific part of the body, then there is no feeling of pain in our mind. Our brain derives this ability in the very long period, become this kind of brain, which can generate thousands of thoughts in a day and we want to stop it that is not possible because if we stop nervous cells, then other activities like controlling kidney, liver, and heart also will be stopped. There is always a dispute in the brain, as the brain may not live if there is no conflict. In the arrays of thoughts, humans are bound to a jailbird. In the Jail of thoughts, the sharp intelligence or learned knowledge is an obstacle which should be forgotten; and if it is separated, then human being can raise ahead of the ease of opinion.

It becomes stronger through the constant efforts of struggle and the struggle to outpace the mind is the mind. Sometimes, you want to stop you're self-talking in your head. When your mind is not taking instruction from you, doing things without your permission. Suppose, if your legs are moving without your consent then it would not be acceptable for you. As if our mind is generating thought without your permission, then it shall not be pleasing for you. But, who is responsible for the generating your thoughts that is unhealthy for you, like that if we intake unhealthy or wrong food, then it may cause stomach diseases or diarrhea to us. Thus, if your lifestyle and surroundings are not authentic and you are living a stressful life which is full of suffering and agony. Then, it may lead to mental disorder. To identify and discover the life, the mind's status is like a calm lake on which no wave is rising. To get conversant with life, the mind should be clear like a mirror on which no dirt is stacked on it. So, anxiety destroyed with the destruction of action, and removal of anxiety destroy lust. Lust-destruction is the salvation that is called liberation or personal freedom.

The idea is that the thought arises from the brain; the pivot of feeling is the heart, the center of the vital force like determination are from the navel. Thought, anxiety, contemplation it is connected to the mind. The emotions like affection, love, hatred, fury, anger, annoyance are occurring from the heart. Vital force arises from the navel. If excessive stress occurs and you focus more on thoughts. The mind is stretched exceptionally intensely. The thought that the string of the harp is so intense that the melody does not arise from them, the strings may break, the human becomes insane, and the human beings have become insane. This thought has become extremely important to make the string of the harp a little bit weak so that they can come in the right direction and the melody can be generated. The state of heart is utterly contradictory to mind. The twine of the heart is loose; if the melody has to be generated, then it needs to make tightened so that it can be in tune too. Anxiety in the twine of thought is to be decreased and the weaker twin of the heart to be tightened. If the string of both thought and feeling are correctly tuned, they are in counterbalanced; then the melody may be created through which the traveling up to navel can be complete.

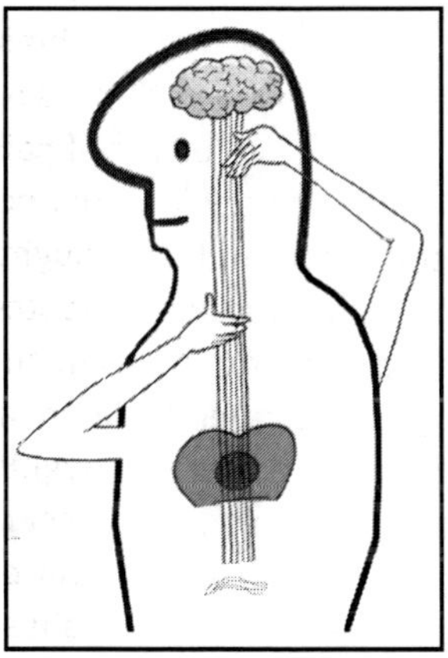

Fig 4.1

State of Passivity and meditation

The conflict in handling our outward etiquette and managing your internal sentiments. Both can affect our consciousness.

There is nothing in the state of complete calmness or passivity. The thoughts are the figure of a buzzing subjugated mind, but they cannot eliminate the ego. They can be quickly ended because they cannot live with passivity. The ego is a vortex point of continuous rotating thoughts has to dissolve in passivity. It is the situation of complete-emptiness, and the meditation is deep, where no mediator in this form, the meditation actually comes into existence.

When you reached the state of meditation, and if there is meditation means you are not. You cannot hold yourselves; you only become a thing among their other items. You are not living a real life; you understand the fact that the acting roles provided to you by someone else. The thoughts are always forming part of others opinions, and their shapes are only masks. They are shapeless. They do not have any authentic existence. Their existence is based on a simulation and their desires. You have to destroy this misconception and false notions; otherwise, it will never be possible for you. The way is only through meditation; it can break this misconception, not by anything else. The mind is the jail; meditation is the only gateway. You will be bound deeper to whatever you want, be free from your desire. On this ground that freedom is not a part of negative and positive thoughts.

Freedom is the superiority of negative and positive thoughts both means free from duality. You need to understand that there is no fight. I think that nobody in this world achieved anything through fighting, except pain or defeat. Don't escape, but try to be awakened? If you are choosing the path of escaping, then you have to keep on surviving. There is no end to it. Awakening is freedom.

Conflict and Health

Conflicts and health attract necessary research on close connections between health and conflict. A lot of public around the world have been caught in the middle of dangerous spirals of the furious conflict and poor health.

The problem of violent conflict investigates the terrible effects on health: injuries due to fighting, long sickness, death rate caused by the breach of public health, the impact on mental health, mental disability affect quality of life. The particular issue evaluates the health outcome of a violent conflict on public talks about ethical issues and societal consequences.

The conflict causes the loss of life, physical injury, common mental disorder, erosion of malnutrition (especially between children), and outbreaks of infectious diseases. It results in a weaker immune system which attracts common preventable diseases, such as flu, cold, cough, diarrhea, sinus, asthma, and serious illnesses give rise to severe pain.

Resilience and Perspective

Resilience is the technique of accepting well in the situation of tragedy, adversity, and threats. There are some situations of stress and disappointment - family and friendship relationship issues, severe health issues, conflicts in the workplace, and financial burden.

When you feel something is going contrary to you and you are facing any trouble, then its resolution is hidden in that trouble too. In this situation, if you find a way from it, that gives you the power to recover from the adversity of life.

Resilience is an essential resource as the individual ability to face, and experiences of adversity strengthen it. The impact of our surrounding, circumstances, and other sources all carry how resilient person are we. It can be learned quickly. It's not only kids learn to change their attitude; adults can choose one option.

Attributes, qualities, and opinion that support resilience is:

- To keep a sense of religious belief or a spiritual dimension,
- The meaning or able to generate motive,

- A sense of Humor,
- A feel of belonging and fellowship,
- Creativity and Flexibility.

Resilient provides the wisdom to know the past and gives the strength to project and plan for the inevitable future. It does not matter if the imagination hopes anything or anyone will make things fascinating.

Being Resilient, we do not stop trying to manage the uncontrollable circumstances. It's better to keep trust in yourself and believe will make it real.

Resilience is pure and an ordinary process, it's not an extraordinary technique. People commonly manifest resilience, but they don't know the facts. An instance in America, ordinary civilians respond to the attacks of terrorist on 11, Sep 2001 and their endeavors helped them to reconstruct their lives once again.

According to Indian Mythology, Ramayana is a known story to everyone that Ravana kidnapped Sita (embodiment of Goddess Lakshmi). The main reason for Ramayana happened. Ravana was the lustful and brutal demon (Rakshasa) king of Lanka. King of Gods Vishnu and God Indra (king of heaven) plan the entire war upon Ravana. To kill Ravana, Sri Rama (who was the incarnation of Lord Vishnu himself) was sent to forests according to all God's cosmic plan. Once again religion and peace will be preserved in the world. Ravana was already charmed by the beauty of Sita. His heart was filled with lust, and he lost all his control. Finally, he abducted her. After this, the war happened between them; Ram defeated Ravana. After killing Ravana; Ram and Sita returned to Ayodhya. The adverse part in this mythology was the kidnapping of Sita. It was planned to kill the Ravana. Even, Ravana was happy because he got salvation from God's hand.

When I started the first job of my career, I faced severe adversity. I overcome this situation where the senior manager was very harsh and non-co-operative. Every time they were involved in the conspiracy and used to try to extort the money from employees. But, I believed that 'adversity is an opportunity.' Whenever I had to face the issue, I always rewarded with the resolution. If you are glaring and authentic, then you ever observe that when we are clear about the issue, then every time problem of your life is disappeared. It is an important thing to understand about life's problems; they are created due to your unclear vision. This way, you have to see it clearly first, then you will get lots of solutions, and then you will be able to use the solutions. No, the process is not too long, it is small and straightforward. The moment you see the problem of your life clear, it disappears.

It is not that you have got the answer, now you will use it, and someday you will succeed in erasing it. The problem was due to your unclear vision. You only created it. Remember, I am not talking about that you have only to watch, what the issue is. I am not saying that if your car gets damaged, then you have to calm down and have to see only what the problem is, the problem is clear, do something now. It does not matter that you sit under the tree and meditate; often open your eyes to watch if the problem has been solved or not. It is not a problem of life; it is a machine problem. If your Car's tire has become punctured, then you have to change the wheel. If you are waiting for someone, then it is not a solution, you have to get up and change the wheel. It does not relate to your brain and your clarity.

The topic of resilience in the psychology of positivity handles with the ability to cope with everything the life throws at you. The person may be knocked down by life, and later he returns as a stronger person than ever before. This kind of person is known as resilient. He endeavors in ways of accepting challenges using internal strength and abilities like belief, hopefulness, true faith, and personal efficacy. To overcome the situation of crisis with resiliency; this level of practicing described as "coming back to the ordinary situation of working."

As a resilient, you can always positively linked to happiness. Resilience is an absolute art of living and screening of science. There is a trust in self in the heart of resilience and this trust something more significant than oneself. The Resilient person does not define adverse circumstances. By understanding the bad times in the form of temporary status, they find themselves moving forward towards a goal; and finding resilience by crossing pain and sorrow.

I still remember my days when I started my job with the company that manufacturing the LED Lights which is located in Bijwasan area of Delhi. During that I had to go through the Dwarka area, in the office timing there is massive traffic congestion on the road of Dwarka and risk of over speed challan is more in Sector 21, Dwarka metro station. I faced this issue two or three times, and the experience was

Fig 4.2

terrible even the traffic police officer didn't want to return my driving license when I was driving above the permitted speed limits of 50 km/h which is the maximum allowed in the most areas of Delhi. After that, I learned the indeed a good driving lesson from that adverse event that almost changed my driving style. Now, the speed of 50 km/h seems like joyful and safe. It requires little concentration on the road, and there is no tension while driving the car.

People look different in their innate ability to handle the stress of life. Anyone can cultivate the resilience; it is feasible to describe yourself as a competent, capable, and strengthening your belief and inner consciousness. And it is crucial that you have probably come back to the previous events and to find all those powers. The resilience is not bound to adulthood. Due to difficulties in childhood, we are growing it, and are starting to rebuild our lives.

As a resilient, it does not make any sense that nobody has to face trouble or anxiety. Emotions like sorrow and pains are usually among those who have suffered great adversity in life. The roadmap of Resilience is involved in considering part of emotional distress.

Resilience is not a feature that either people have choice or not. It includes conduct, opinion, concern, ideology, and other acts that can be conversant and evolved in anybody.

The members of the troubled family can cause harm to the other members of the family or outsiders may be. But, resilient people are ready to face such issues to check and respond actively and constructively liable. Their pre-effective responses to adverse conditions are repeated over the time, become self-powered into their inner selves. To that extent, it is conversant, as the resilience cultivated out of the challenge to hold up the confidence and dignity. The resilient avoid us from blaming ourselves for anything terrible or erroneous. In the psychological language, they are observer or evidence of blame. They are empowered to touch the success and attainments, be responsible for all right and wrong things in their present life. The habit of a resilient person is turned up to give honest answers. They take the initiatives, the charge of issues, examining itself, and make the necessary actions about understanding the fact up to the level of satisfaction.

Features of Resilience

The main essence in the resilience is displaying kindness and concern for others. The parity and supportiveness within casual relationships, close family relationships, business relationship, and any outside the family relationship. Relationships that make faith, believe, and love. It provides advice, boost, and assurance. Strengthen one person's resilience.

Some others factors are related with resilience are:

- Your positive attitude and belief in your abilities and power.
- Skill and ability to create realistic plans. Take the vital steps to move forward.
- Capabilities to manage strong emotions and passions.
- Talent in issue handling and competent in coordination and communication.

These all elements assist people in developing it by oneself.

A Strategy of Building Resilience

Building resilience is own experience. In a painful event and a troubled life, everyone cannot respond positively. The technique of creating the resilience that works for a person, sometimes it does not work for another person. A person's nature can effect on what kind of feelings and adverse circumstances. One Person can use different strategies. There are different ways to develop resilience, and the several approaches may be appropriate for your plan.

Boost your positivity

The resilient people experience both positive and negative feeling in life's difficulties or stressful situations. They will also find a way to look good in adverse condition. They assume in this circumstances, 'Well, at least I do not have to face any other major problem.'

Due to the mechanisms of underlying abilities of the brain, our brains are naturally wired to pay more attention to adverse incidents than positive ones.

Because of built-in survival mechanisms, our brain naturally pays more attention to negative thoughts over the positive ones. The resilient person is not pumping on negative feeling, but rather than to observe as a shred of evidence so letting them go. They maintain a balance between the proportion of negative and positive thoughts.

Create Humor

Laughing tends to reduce stress to more moderate levels. The good sense of humor helps us to rebound. In the case of comedic intelligence, we need to use people to laugh and joke. I believe that it helps you to understand deeply about pain relief, makes people happy in both the mind and the body.

Achieve optimism

Pull and achieve practical optimism. It is a belief that we can do self-improvement and do work to make things more useful for us. If you exercise realistic optimism, it helps you deal with challenges because they work and do better to do so. Achieve optimism correlates with a higher degree of resiliency.

Choose a healthy diet and engage in exercise daily

It's better to pick a healthy food and maintain the healthy weight and daily intake calories in range of 2000kcal – 2500kcal depending on the gender, age, metabolic rate, daily exercise, and activities. Follow the regular exercise program in everyday life which is a significant source against anxiety and depression. If we care about our self which assists to keep our mind and body primed to deal with situations that require resilience.

Create a relationship and maintain social networks

Make good association with fellows, family members, friends, and others. Keep help and support them who trust and care about you, it strengthens our resilience. Many people search to remain active in social groups, and other people find local groups to choose social support and help each other at the time of need.

Adapt flexibility and move forward to achieve goals and objective

Accept changes that help you make adjustments with the situations, and you can change it. Some targets and goals could not be further achievable due to adverse circumstances. Generate many practical purposes. Do things on a regular basis, which looks like a small accomplishment that assists you to achieve your goals.

Learn from experience

If you pay attention to your past life and focus on the lines of your abilities and strength, which will be helpful in discovering new strategies for constructing resilience.

Resilience and Mental health

Resilience can save us from several adverse conditions such as stress, depression, and confliction of mind. It may assist in offset grounds that magnify the risk of mental health diseases. The connection between good health and illness needs higher attention to focus. Resilience serves a defending team, which allows individuals to get success at the time of adversity. Improve your resilience power in the treatment of diseases is an essential objective. We describe the complex chain of events related to host resistance in infectious disease then we try to reorganize present intellect around a specific idea and conceptions to explain possible points for boosting resilience and perfect mental health.

'Thank God for blessing me the power of Resilience.'

Chapter - 5

Forgiveness – Getting to Health

Forgiveness carries peace of mind and free from the feeling of rage and irritation. It is not a feeling. If this happens, then we rarely forgive others. Although there has been some debate on whether there is a need for a positive attitude towards the culprit for real forgiveness, experts believe that at least it involves deep negative emotions.

Forgiveness does not mean to forget and nor does it mean to cancel or debate the crime. Though, forgiveness can help to improve the broken relationship. However, it does not force you to reconcile with the person who has hurt or harmed you or released him with legal responsibility. In this way, it enables you to recognize that agony that causes you to suffer without defining pain, which can help you to correct your life and move on.

If, we study the historical analysis and cultural reference in which Jesus lived and focused on forgiveness. The great Jesus or Jesus Christ is originators of Christianity; it was believed that he was the son of God.

Jesus Christ was born in the village of Bethlehem in Jerusalem. His father's name was Joseph and mother's name was Mary. As he grew up, his attention started moving towards God. At the age of thirty years, Jesus came from Galilee to the Jordan; John baptized him. When he went up out of the water, a voice from heaven said, "This is my Son, whom I love; with him, I am well pleased." Since then, he began preaching his messages and true knowledge of Jewish religion to the people of Israel.

Jesus taught us to worship God, love all human beings, and behave with others as you would like them to do with you. He valued the simplicity and purity of the heart. Because of the popularity of Jesus Christ, some people became jealous of him, and they provoked the rulers in Jerusalem, that Jesus is organizing the people against pride and the state. After this, the life sentence was given to Jesus. The soldiers placed the nails into his feet and hands. He was hanged on the hook. The time of the pain of the death of Jesus Christ, he said in his prayer to God about his opponents (the words of Jesus Christ) - "Lord, forgive them, for they do not know what they are doing." Jesus believed in forgiveness. At the time of his death on the cross, his sentiments were love and mercy for the inept people. But, he was the only person who is one without sin.

Forgiveness recognizes as a sign of weakness in our society, as people may do not wish to forgive because they do not want to give the primacy to other in the rapport. When I read an article on forgiveness, I always found myself was confused, and it took time to understand the illusion, and the manner in which I came to know about forgiveness. I still remember the event when I went to Mayapuri in Delhi where one of the clients is manufacturing accessories of Camera. When, I had accidentally kept my lunch box on the Table, which is not considered as a safe place as everyone is used to visit that place. So, after sometime when I came back to the table for my lunchbox, my lunchbox was not available in that place. The employees working there were intelligent and smart. They told me that you have to care about your belongings, otherwise, in this way you can lose your things. They returned my lunch very modestly and felt sorry for the inconvenience. I was so confused about the situation that whether I would apologize or thanked for teaching me a good lesson about the etiquettes and courtesy. Now, I was more aware of forgiveness. The reality says that forgiveness is not a sign of weakness. A lot of strength is needed to accept suffering to manifest and forgive it. However, if you are putting so much faith in forgiving powers, instead of helping you, it can harm you to a great extent.

An apology is not about the altering of past; it's about modifying the future. Forgiveness accepts the past and finds it to focus in the future.

An Apology is the process of healing, and the person always enjoys benefits like high dignity, better attitude, a frame of mind and keep the relationships bond strong. This is a decision when you accept someone to pardon, embrace, and grow.

Forgiveness grants us to detach our mind and our body. You can transform yourselves a more amiable, humble and gracious. Forgiveness reduces the stress hormone and boosts the aptitude and immune function. We realize more focused, peaceful, relaxed, and when we opt forgiveness for good, then we very rarely get an illness.

Forgiveness and Relationships

Forgiveness never means trust, given independently, and faith must be obtained. The faith usually created with constant telling truth to someone over a period. I feel that in any regards or relationship, the best form of affection and friendship is forgiveness. It needs a strong person who can forgive, and if any person wants to make a confession or accept apologies, then it needs great courage and pure heart.

Forgiveness is always helpful and favorable effect on every kind of relationships, whether it is a business, professional, friendship, romantic, family, relationship. In going on interrelationship, for giveness is just different; a current partner can make things worse or transcend. A person can forgive more if they have faith and consent for his partner.

On every occasion, it associated with ample prosperity and greater well-being, particularly in healthy relationships instead of weak commitment. And people utilize many ways like filling the questionnaire, revoke previous relationships, and evaluate their current relationships.

What will people get? If they are not ready to sacrifice, and they want to avenge, instead of forgiveness - they often face negative emotions like the struggle, conflict, and weak ability to compromise. I asked many people to recall particular wrongdoing or the offense wherein anyone harmed them, and then I asked about their intentions for revenge. The many persons who opted for revenge had less level of satisfaction in the relationship. On the other hand, the person who was set out to forgive, they enjoyed a healthier relationship and longer life commitment in relationships.

If we see the contribution of forgiveness about marriage relations, then it maintains a strong bond between you and your partner. The higher if we invest in the relationship, we need a list of useful strategies that guide us during the crisis. These strategies help to determine happiness and satisfaction. Whenever, companion hurts one another, which means that the change in the intention of their relationship. They had earlier undying and unconditional love. Now, they are not ready to cooperate rather then they preferred to betray. Instead, of enjoying each other, why do they suddenly become more non-observant? They focus on losing side rather than on understanding and compromises. They may use their past misdeed to recall his or her failure. Forgiveness helps to relieve relationships more liberal, remove conflicts and fulfill their aim of association.

The Science of forgiveness &Health benefits of forgiveness.

The researchers are concerned with observing the stuff of forgiveness as a medical procedure. Researcher's evidence is manifesting that if you keep the troublesome memories and resentments in a long period, then you may have to face health issues.

Base on scientific observations forgiveness has numerous ways for your physical and mental health improvements. It cut down stress, disappointments, and lower down the heart attack risk. Hatred and unforgiveness always find a path for poor health and illness. Ignorance and Unforgiveness can weaken the immune system.

For example, unforgiveness inhibits the production of essential hormones in our cells and weakens the way to fight against harmful microbes, bacteria, viruses, and infectious diseases.

In the studies, forgiveness has a relationship between mental health and physical health. It plays a vital role in the relationship and overall health. If we find forgiveness in the brain area, it is deep-rooted in centers of emotions, which is commonly known as the limbic rather than the cortex area related to the rational decision. Some finders noted down and recorded the pictures of their brain motions and activities. If the people were sympathetic or forgiving, the similar areas have been lit up in the brain emotion centers, and when the same people experienced the feeling of the crime and revenge, then the emotion centers stop actively working. It could be a hint for the interventionists.

I believe that we can understand forgiveness depends on the context. It does not relate to the modifying or upgrading an individual, their conduct, or their deeds. In some cases, we do not want continuous relations then the presence of apology starts decreasing, retaliation, and anger become strong. Therefore, unforgiving can be considered as a negative emotional state where an annoyed person keeps feelings of anger, hate and hostility, never forgets his attacker. He doesn't want to replace his negative feeling and does not like sympathy and compromise.

Usually, people deal with forgiveness with different persons based on their criteria of understanding, which can be chosen by them as they get justification accordingly. They do injustices in various manners. They decided that they don't want to forgive, and they don't need to alter their feeling. But, if they are not interested in changing somehow, then unforgiveness affect adversely on mental, physical, and relational health. The people should think over the person to whom they misbehaved, denied or hurt them. When they think about their past offense, and if we monitored their heart, blood pressure rate, and sweat gland, then we found that their blood pressure and heart rate is increased, they felt more perspiration at that time. It caused them to feel disappointed, distracted, restless, and uneasy. Forgiveness provides various health advantages like:

1. Reduction in anxiety

Pardon relieves from fear and sorrow as you may not have further any thoughts for imagination that create stress. It helps yourself as part of healing and follows to leave annoyance and anxiety backside.

2. Great religious well-being

If you choose any religion, then forgiveness will bring you closer to your religion. Every religion teaches on this earth to help others by extending our hand to help somebody which is more than any prayer by joining two hands. If we allow ourselves to be forgiven, it provides peace and love; then this is the right part of treatment.

3. Control high Blood pressure

It offers normal conditions in many body processes and helps in the smooth flow of our heart's respiratory system and the circulatory system. When we feel less stress due to improvements in past experiences of forgiveness, then our heart rate can be better than before.

4. Reduce enmity and results in better anger management system

Apology prevents behavior of hatred and enmity. The action which causes road rage and choosing other reasons for fighting, resulting in a lesser sense of apology. It is better to keep yourself calm in such a negative situation. If we want more self-control and needs to get rid of anger, then it is better to apologize to anyone in anger.

5. More friendships

When we're holding forgiveness in our life, we can come close to friends and family. It provides an opportunity to change old relationships or extend it further. This helps you to enter into a new relationship - all because we have made a place for them with forgiveness.

6. Improved relations

When we adopt forgiveness a regular part of daily life, then we begin to note that our relations with our colleagues, family members and neighbors begin to flourish. There's far less drama to deal with, that's a grand bonus in life.

7. Psychological Goodness

Forgiveness elevates the psychological well-being and better mental status that helps in living a life of joy and purposefully. By freeing yourself from complaints, it helps to become more coherent at all levels. We become peaceful, happy, and want to give love and compassion to everyone in this world. Most of us hope for forgiveness without knowing how to create it.

> 'You forgive people simply because you still want them in your life.' -- Char Boivin

Chapter - 6

Importance of Friendship in our life

Friendship is pure love, respect, worship, nothing is asked here, and it happens automatically. In friendship, we consider another person more important than ourselves, and we always ready to sacrifice, whenever it is needed. It is not a deal or business. It may be possible only when friends are real, faithful, and authentic or they are fully aware of themselves. If the love, trust, and affection do not come out of this awareness, then it is not a real friendship, and it never changes in the opposite situation, the fact is that there is nothing adverse here.

My idea is that nothing should be said, unlike the enemy because the enemy can become a friend tomorrow, then it may be the most embarrassing moment for you. Furthermore, it can be a clear perception that at any moment the ordinary friendship may turn into enmity. It is an unconscious state of mind, where hatred is just behind the love, at that time you love the same person, and the same moment you hate him also, you do not know this.

To get the taste of friendship, you will need a significant change in it. Friendship is indeed, pure itself, and I can't say it is a bloom, I can say only that it is a fragrance of a flower. I can sense it; even our two hands are not enough to feel it and, it always gives the awesome feeling and happiness to everyone. I cannot say to you that this question is extremely complicated. You are still not coming to a point where friendship can change your experience. If, you are concrete and precise so you will know a perfect love – only the fragrance of love always around you.

Friendship is a distinct relationship which is not an agreement; it is not spoken or relieved. This is not limited to person-specific; though it is related with entire existence and the man is only a small part of it. It can happen with whole existence whether it is a star, mountain, trees, water, animal, or something else that can be included in friendship. However, maybe you are an enlightened person like "Buddha" or may be equivalent to "Mahatma Gandhi," it does not mean that no one can be your opponent. Although, your success, happiness, or peace will be troubling any other person without understanding you and many people become your enemy without any reason.

In fact, the awakened or enlightened person may have more enemies than the other person. The unenlightened person has only some opponents, the awakened person facing the opponent almost the entire world. In this way, an enlightened person promotes the arrogance of several people, and they can become jealous or angry because of their wealth and reputation.

If we say that the enlightened person does not have any enemy, it means that from his point of view, he has no enemies. However, if we consider the interest of other persons, the higher the popularity of an enlightened person, the more they will be against him. This is happening for centuries like this.

Important in Friendship

Friendship comprises the essence of eternal and coolness – Friendship makes everything is pretty. If friendship is the essence of loyalty and it cannot be transformed. In the relationship of friendship, there should be a coolness. In the climate of friendship, it is followed endlessly does not involve mood and hatred. It always requires love, and you love that person unconditionally, it need not struggle, and it does not go high and low have more essence of eternal quality.

Friendship is more unknowingly - We must feel the happiness in the joy of others, and you celebrate with someone for any reason; it is entirely not an absurdity. You have to move ahead as it is rooted in mind, have to filter it gradually. If you love a person, try to make it a friendship, it will be more sustainable. In this way, there would be more happiness, association, communication, and unity.

Friendship is worth more than love - In, love the subsequent stage is friendship. Love has to go through friendship. In a relationship, love is a preliminary step and friendship is the last step.

Friendship is spiritual and meditative - Friendship has nothing to do with passion, it inclines to compassion. Love is bound to trouble because the essence of jealousy is. Friendship is more concerned with non-jealous: you can become friends of many people, be friendly with the entire existence. Envy of anyone is not involved here, so friendship is vast and more spiritual.

It is difficult to see love is growing in a wife and husband relationship. Regarding marriage, it is difficult to see love in every partner at every stage of life. It is awful, as you love your partner, and you live with the same person, the romance is not growing.

According to my belief and experience is that love is just like the easy starters for dinner parties or only as a passion for purchasing a new car. Your starter or passion cannot run a whole show. Before the purchasing of a new car, you always dream about the same. When you first start the car, this moment was full of joy. After few days this happiness did not exist, love and desire are missing, which was earlier very strong; now you are driving the same car the only engine is working, emotions are not running in mind. Love should function as a whole show; it's bound to fail; that's why friendship is forever. When love fails, a friendship begins to grow. If there is love, make sure friendship is increasing or not because later on romance will not appear and if the friendship does not increase at that time, then the whole thing becomes flat.

In the beginning, love happened between the partners with the fantastic imagination, zest, and passion. They introduce themselves in love with great aspiration and hope. But, after sometime love is gone. I don't know why they don't listen to their heart or follow the instructions of a brain and everything becomes ugly, nasty, and one manages in any way, shows pietism.

According, to my opinion love is merely a starter; don't feel to rely on it. It's needed to start the car. When the car has started then we need not depend on the starter, further friendship is a fuel which runs the car on its own.

Before the romance going out, we have to confirm that friendship is already landed if the work of love is over has played the game very well, and the possibility of friendship should be increased at level. Subsequently, nothing is left for frustration. Friendship is not an illusion; it is a moment of high melody, remain on the top forever. Love your partner as much as possible, ready to give space to friendship.

The benefits of friendship

Friendship has a significant influence on happiness and health. It's not easy to build or maintain friendships. Friendship is a big term having a big network that includes relatives, friends, and other relationships that ever supports you in strengthening your physical health. Several people visit and create sound networking. Regardless of your age or situation, it does not delay developing new pals, reunite with old contacts, and look approachable and boost their social life, mental health status, and overall happiness.

Due to the general demands of a busy life or due to stress in the daily life of my friend and others loved ones. First, I was scared. Later, I tried to contact the people I love most. In a short span of time, as per my list of things to remember - I contacted my close friends and my family members. Some text chat with my friends turned my anxiety into humor, and others family member changed my feeling to cry. However, not everyone, some colleagues in the office confident about true love and friendship. With the conversation with each friend and colleagues who provided a supportive sign, I started feeling better.

The strong relationship forever creates better health results, enjoy advantages like the longevity of life, stop fearing diseases, maintain an existing relationship, and improve social life. Friendships need endeavor and time; best friends can:

- **Make you're feeling better** - Enjoying a good time with positive friends can bring great pleasure and boost your positive attitude.
- **Stand with you in the darkest moments of life -** Good friends help you in every moment of life - relationship breakups, loss of a job, serious illness, and death of loved ones. They channelize the energy in a positive direction and keeps shining with you in the rest of your life.
- **Reduce your stress and depression** - Good friends provide you strength from inside. In friendship, a friend can help reduce the feeling of loneliness which is essential for stress and anxiety.
- **Increase the prospects of success -** Good friends help in improving life. They can provide technical guidance, strengthening willpower and increase the prospects of success.
- **Help you like regardless of age** - Good friends assist you in identify the idea and stay open for you the highest good for all concerned. They prevent you from doing things that hurt

you, often do not leave you isolated in old age, and act as a buffer against the hardship of life, depression, revaluation of priorities, making the best memories of life.

'My parents are my best friends.'

Chapter - 7

Humor - Important for your health

This is authentic that humor is a part of the mind, and a chief ingredient in all facets of self-care and health boosting.

There, it is a sense of humor if we feel in our mind, and if you are out of mind, then we also feel humorous. All are varied in all qualities. For instance, if you see a small kid whose mind has not been fully grown – yes, you can easily make the child giggle by touching on his foot or belly. Now, the role of the mind is not actively involved in it, only touched the sensitive portion of the body which is having a sense of humor.

Most of the humor is caused due to the imaginations, misconceptions or because of real events – which is related to mind and body deeply. Cracking of jokes is suddenly turning up your mood and always make a funny appeal. The science of fun is that it leads you to a certain height of hope and suddenly there is a turn that you never expected. Humor is a powerful tool for managing conflict and reducing tension when the negative feeling is high side.

Laughter elevates mood, reduces fear and coping with illness

Laughter usually occurs in the social life of peoples, spreads rapidly through the brains of peoples who intended for the always for a joke. This is an excellent tool which prevents any stress that usually exists among the people and mutually. It is a signal of purposeful connection and association.

It elevates a mood and help in reducing the nervousness, uneasiness, work pressure, and intensity of mind. A person with laughter can easily cope with the disease, can surround himself with romance, passion, and kindness. The blast of your laughter is usually gathering your entire stress in mind. It helps friends, life partners, and family members can get away from disagreements and convey in a manner which develops our association and relationship, instead of breakups and conflicts.

Laughter should be intensive and may not be acute. This is a kind of remedy that I set in life for harshness and seriousness. Everyone may prefer medicine of seriousness in their life. But, it does not work at all. You have to be a little stupid. In reality, the highest peak of intelligence always stays in it, the greatest masterminds in the world were also the biggest idiot. It would be difficult to understand. You never think that they can be stupid because your brain is always divided and says that an intelligent person can never be stupid; and stupid can never be a smart person. Both views are not correct. The acceptance of stupidity in mind enjoys wisdom.

Laughter can be considered as spiritual health. While laughing, you can separate your mind very readily. For me, laughter holds the highest value in a person's life. However, every Religion is focusing the seriousness, and because of their insistence, the whole world is mentally ill.

I can understand that only the human being is capable of a laugh in this world, this means that laughter is the highest point of development. I want you to assume a prayer that is laugh because when you are entirely laughing, then you are in the extent. You cannot laugh in the future. Even, you cannot change the past. All the societies have developed obstacles for all mankind. It means "suck the juice out of life," and all the smile and laughter have been pulled out. Everyone into disqualification.

I want once people try to lose the temper, and they can laugh as much as possible, or just like the lion's roar. Even, then laughter turns a beautiful experience. However, never let it turns hype because once it becomes hype, its value becomes zero because it shall be wisdom at its pinnacle. Although I do not want to play seriously, it is possible with a pretty laugh. Your laugh, your playfulness is the belief that you have to understand it. Your solemnity depicts that you have not only missed it and even equally misinterpret it – considering the seriousness is not more than except illness.

Sorrowfulness is one more name of seriousness, it pursues darkness of end of life, and my life does not want all this at all.

The Smile lights up the attitude and provide assistance in good feeling and stay mentally healthy.

A smile is an effective mood booster. Since, my childhood, my parents continued to see a smile on a face. Even my parents never forget that their child's first smile is in the room. Like a laugh, smiles are transmissible, and in life, people shall never miss the moments that make you smile, and we shall encourage everyone to share it with all.

Activity in the nucleus accumbens, which is a part of the brain, shows that the smile is connected to the positive feeling, reward, and gratitude. This brain area, especially in the left hemisphere is related to reward reactions. Undoubtedly, the smile looks good on a face and is good for your health too. Smiling is always receive a reward response, a reference to social attachment, and obstruction for unnecessary stress and depression.

Smiles assist in staying mentally healthy. Laughter makes you feel better. When you laugh, after laughing, you look good. A smile is not only a relief from pain and sorrow it also assists to have a hopeful, courage, and strength affirmatory approach in cumbersome circumstances.

It primes our mind, prepares us to joke and get involved in the fun. Once, we start laughing, it not only reduces your stress, it also brings changes in your body like

- **Smile** increase energy, and muscles relaxed for a few minutes. We can accomplish our work in a more focused way.
- Humor intensifies intake of breathing. It activates many organs of body - heart, lungs, muscles, and brain.
- When you start laughing, you cannot feel anxiety, disappointment and irritated. It cools down our tensions.
- **It** improves our blood flow and controls our blood pressure. It helps in improving heart rate and **safeguard our heart** against a heart attack.
- **Laughing helps in burning calories.** It may burn 40 calories in 10 to 20 minutes - which is sufficient to lose one to two Kg over a period.
- **Humor assists in the longevity of life**. It helps in battling of all kind of diseases.
- **Laughter attracts others** which can have a profound impact on all facet of mental and physical health. It always looks at the funny side and resolves the conflicts without holding sulkiness and hatred.
- **Humor makes the immune system stronger like** increases antibodies of infection-fighting and white blood cells of the body. It **triggers** the body's natural good feeling chemicals, temporarily relieves pain, and promote overall well-being.

Bring more laughter into your life

Laughter is the sweetest medicine and birth right of every human being. Babies start smiling after the birth of first weeks, and they laugh loudly within the one month of being born. Suppose, if you have not grown up in a house where laughter is an ordinary sound. But, you can uncover laughing at any level of life. You can start by separating the particular time frame to seek laughter and build from there. After all, we want to include humor into the fabric of our lives, seeking it naturally in whatever we can do.

Have Fun in the Parlance

The best way is to bring humor in normal conversation and have to develop a habit of seeking amusement in a stressful situation. See also public speakers who maintain the sense of humor in their speeches. You can ask "What's the funniest thing that happened to you today?"

Spend your time with Funny people

You have to consider yourself a humorous person. Choose your companion and friends who like to have fun and make others laugh. Start enjoy your company with those peoples who laugh easily regularly find humor in everyday events.

Fully aware about of yourself

Be completely conscious of your body and fully aware about of yourself. You have to measure how many hours you are aware of yourself in a day. Time should be going to increase day by day. By doing this, you are connected with your present and consider the funny and good things in your life. That will distance you from negative thoughts and the dark side of the life which, otherwise, hinders happiness. After a few months of practice, you will learn how to ignore yourself with negative thoughts; you will be free from many diseases related to body and mind. Make a list when you're in a state of sadness, you have further to travel to get to humor and laughter. Knowing awareness and alertness is big steps towards "happiness."

Simulated laughter therapy

A famous psychologist from Santa Barbara, California who discovered simulated laughter therapy. It is a set of technique that uses laughter for relief from strong negative emotions, counterbalance the chemistry of emotions, and heal the mind, body, and soul.

To add simulated laughter into your life, search for laugh therapy groups in the local park when you go for morning or evening walk, you can laugh at other people's jokes, even if you do not like them too funny. It will make both people feel good, keep your relations healthy. I suggest you if you do not find it funny, then believe it will good for you as the real thing. It helps in burning calories just like an exercise; it is more productive and entertaining.

Other opportunities to laugh

- Read funny pages of Newspaper and magazines.
- Watch Comedy movies, TV shows, and YouTube videos.
- Tell a funny story and jokes to children's.
- Check out your comic books and other articles have humor sections.
- Join "laughter yoga" classes and invite friends to go to a comedy club.
- Spend time for fun activities, music, dance, etc.

Is Humor Important for Your Health?

The well-known fact about the humor is that it has a favorable effect on your health. There are various beliefs noticing health benefits connected with laughter. Every person on this earth accepted that fun and smile on a face always help in the protection of any disease whether it is related to body or mind. The good sense of humor always boost your immunity system and provides the same benefits as physical work out. Laughter can assist you with various diseases. There is a lack of comprehensive research to support affirmations. Majority of claims about the health blessings of laughter have limited scientific facts and are grounded in unfounded studies.

Most facts on health lived shortly. Some people confounded with the effect of humor on health benevolence. Some useful types of researches show that health benefits of humor, especially concerning stress. For instance, Norman Cousins, suffering from a severe form of arthritis. He developed his recovery program and recovered from it by watching comedy films and positive attitude toward illness. He was always optimistic, known for his gentleness and his intense love of life for himself and others. He said that "I made the joyous discovery that ten minutes of genuine belly laughter had an anesthetic effect and would give me at least two hours of pain-free sleep, when the pain-killing effect of the laughter wore off, we would switch on the motion picture projector again and not infrequently, it would lead to another pain-free interval." His confrontation with that disease is elaborated in the book "Anatomy of an Illness as Perceived by the Patient."

Fun and good comedy are useful for reducing anxiety; some people say it is not a long-term and permanent solution. It may boost your immune system. It does not provide any guarantee that it will come with long-run benefits. If, we find that laughter is associated with health advantages and the connection between laughter and health is useful. The researches in connection with humor revealed that the existence of humor enhanced the positive feeling and increased pain tolerance. One of the main part of the analysis that it needs to be a focus on humor have some analgesic effect, as a result of the entertainment of comedy movie and enjoyment of the joke, it releases endorphins in our brain. These endorphins connect with the receptors in the brain which reduce our feeling of pain. Even it stimulates a positive atmosphere in our body. So, Humor can hold the keys for any health benefits.

Humor helps to meet your life's challenges.

Comedy and the ability to make fun with others not only makes life more enjoyable, but also helps in resolving your conflicts, maintain social networking, and become more creative.

Those who include humor in their daily lives, they find that it is a sign of psychological health and all their relationships with favorable happiness is associated with positive feelings.

Life introduces challenges that can focus on the sphere of imagination. When you face any conflict in your life and treat yourself seriously. You think out of the box, and it can be challenging to find new solutions. However, if we start playing with the issues to resolve the conflicts, we can easily convert it into an opportunity for success and creative learning. Children usually play with their problems. In the beginning, they are confused and are always afraid. Suddenly, their problems turn into a game, they play with a sense of control and find new ways to solve the issues.

Interacting with others in playful ways helps not only examining positive outcomes associated with stressful life transitions, and it also enables you to retain this creative ability.

'My life is full of fun'

Chapter - 8

LOVE – Re-touch your Life

Love is absolutely liberal, permeable and vulnerable. You don't know how to love. It happens, you do not need to present it; it comes by chance, it's one of the depths. If any person does not fall in love, then the right issue is how to love. What you think is love, it is not real love. The love you understand is an organic urge; it relies upon your hormones and chemistry. It can be easily separated - a slight transformation in your alchemy and the love that you believed was "very much reality" will be easily gone. You are saying attraction or lust is "love." This discrimination must be noticed.

The love associated with reality arises from consciousness or out of your innermost being - not from your body. Lust arises from your body, not from consciousness. You have confined the love to one person, which means that you are addressing someone. Although, love is not based on an event that can be confined. You cannot keep it in your fist, you can feel it in your open hands. During the time your fist is closed, they are empty. But, once your hands are open, the whole existence is available to you.

Understanding Pure Love and Simple Love

The word "Love" comes from a Sanskrit word 'Lobha.' 'Lobha' Refers to 'Greedy.' There should be some secret or any alchemical factor behind it. In fact, greediness or seduction becomes love. When, 'Lobha' or 'Greed' absorbed adequately, which later converted into love.

PURE LOVE	SIMPLE LOVE
Unpretentious	Pretentious
It means sharing, never ask for whatsoever in return.	Only demand & never gives.
it energizes your intellect and soul.	Becomes weak due to sentiments.

Love is sharing. It means only giving and never ask for whatsoever in return. It's sharing unconditionally with everyone. Lust or Greed is hoarding, only demand and never gives. Both come on its own accord. In love, whoever comes close to you will feel the friendliness. Pure love is an entirely different experience. Ordinary love is an urge or demand. Pure love is about sharing. It does not understand anything about the demand, knows the joy of giving. Pure love is non-pretentious and straightforward. Ordinary love always pretends too much. It almost sweetened with syrup what we say 'lovey-dovey' or becomes ill or weak due to sentiments. Pure love is nutrition or nourishment; it energizes your intellect and soul. The simple love feeds your selfhood. It is better to have some intellectual awareness and experience about the truthiness of love as it can provide the full taste of the beauty, attractiveness, sanctity, and reality. Love never waits for being honored, rewarded, even thanks or to be granted. If thankfulness comes from the other side, love is always astonishing - it is a pleasant surprise because there was no hope. If the gratitude comes from the other hand, love is always astounded - it is a charming surprise, as there was no anticipation. You never feel disappointed in pure love because of no expectation involved in it. Although, there Is full aspiration is rooted in ordinary love and even you can't fulfill all demands as whatsoever is done always falls short. Its expectation is huge; no one can satisfy it. As a result, ordinary love attracts disappointments, and real love achieves satisfaction and happiness. Similarly, food is needed for the body; love is the nourishment for our mind and soul. It is not possible to live without food, and in this manner, the soul is weak without love. Sometimes, there is a different climate in love; it may be possible that hatred comprises in love at the same time. When you love that person, you can also hate the person; the constant struggle is a part of it. This is the key to life if a person accepts himself as without an ego, attracts others in love, even almost everything in this world.

Love yourself and forever

The first step in pure love is to love yourself.

The person who respects himself and loves himself can also honor others with his heart because he knows that "Just like I am, so are others. Just as I enjoy dignity and love, so do others." For instance, the enlightened person has no enemies, no friends and no relative, only real love, without any complications. He is constantly sharing his love for everyone who is next available for it. That is genuine and authentic love. On the other hand, the politicians just because of their greediness stop people loving themselves and have destroyed their capacity to love. Whatever they think that love will be proxy or that can be duty, not love.

In India, even families are fulfilling their duties. Mothers and father fulfill their responsibilities and duties for their children. Therefore, in return, they expect that children will fulfill their duties towards their parents. Similarly, in husband and wife relationship, wives are always loyal to their duties toward their husband and so they expect the same condition as their husbands to fulfill his responsibilities for his wife. There is a condition of the wedding that's why she should always be your wife; if it turns unconditional, she will never be your wife. You are living a life with conditions and only to fulfill specific duties, and conditions; will life happen. Do you perceive that love is really in your life or you undergo for a mutual welfare strategy? "I will provide you this, and you will be going to share with me that. If you are unable to give me this, I will not share you that." If it is a mutual welfare plan, we are accepting it very ravishingly. So, where is love? When you talk about Love, it does not know anything about duty or conditions. Condition and Duty only bring us, responsibilities and formalities.

Lovers never feel that they have obliged the other. On the other hand, they believe that due to love only, I am obliged. They never thought that they had done enough; they feel that it was possible more. Love is an ecstasy, a sharing; not formal. If you can see at everything fondly then, the entire world becomes so beautiful in your eyes. You must realize that love is not somewhat that you can do.

If a person loves himself and enjoys it immensely then, it becomes blissful and begins overflowing, even reaching others. If I'm living a life with love, I have to share it. If you are loving yourself that does not mean that being alone is better, even if you cannot enjoy your whole life yourself. If you believe that love is a light which becomes beautiful to share and you are feeling joyful and nothing much with ego. Actually, love is a wonderful feeling that the gloom of the ego will not go with the moonlight of love. Firstly, focus illumination of love for yourself. Let the love eliminate your inward obscurity and feebleness and then focused on others. And once our mind and soul becomes strong and love is the way that will take them beyond time. Therefore, lovers are never afraid of death, and they begin to believe that their love is immortal.

Love opens the gateway to meditation. Only a person whoever loves himself can enjoy the calm meditative state or else can always escape or avoiding himself. I have seen that people are regularly looking for someone else. At first, they do not want to stay with themselves. They are always looking for companions; they want to ignore with themselves. They usually spent time in cinemas or in their own home to watch something which is entertaining or reading novels and same newspaper repeatedly or play chess and other games on mobiles to keep themselves updated or busy. Even, they become so frustrated with himself that they are ready to go with someone for their lust, whether she is a prostitute. They are wasting their time in absurdity and as a result, distorted the devotion of inner beauty and burned their eyes on useless porn videos. They don't have enough time to enjoy inner happiness.

Every newborn is like a blank paper. As soon as this child starts to grow, the child becomes unbalanced and it gets distorted in different ways and does not reach the true love. Although my urge is love, it starts with you; later it can spread to others. Its further spread spontaneously; we don't have to spread it. The great Enlighted person Gautama Buddha shows the path for meditation. He emphasized perfection to practice meditation. Firstly, pay attention to loving yourself and then watch. If you don't love with yourself and start seeing, then it is far from mediation and morality. Many followers made the same mistake that they do not focus on the first part of the sutra. They try to jump straightly on the next step "Watch yourself." Love makes it possible to feel oneself, and it is a correct way to understand oneself. Generate power, strength, and intensity of love around you. In this universe, love all creatures and systems, body, mind, soul, and everything. "Love" itself means acceptance. You need not to suppress. You suppress when you dislike anything.

Don't suppress, because if you suppress, then you cannot create Eye-to-Eye contact with our beloved ones and not able to look into your own eyes or reality. Be aware and attentive, do not be unconscious. Do not behave in a sleeping manner. Do not work like a gadget or a robot or any human-made machine.

In reality, we live life unconsciously. We do not say words carefully, and we are not cautious about what we are saying and doing, we are not careful about our action. People keep on presuming, not interested in seeing or do not have any insight. Insight develops entirely through awareness and watchfulness; after that, we can look ourselves even with shut eyes. Currently, we cannot look even with our open eyes. Our brain is constantly thinking, and we are always engaged in projecting. Our mind keeps interfering with reality, proving a new imagination with new shape, melody, and color and design its own accord. Our mind not always allows us to watch what reality, the average brain of human-being generates around fifty thousand thoughts per day, and it is estimated that seventy percent of these thoughts are not positive. It repeatedly sends warnings and negative signals that we do not want to receive. The scientists usually consider that our senses like ears, nose, eyes, tongue and other senses, and our mind is the basis of reality. However, the entire assumptions are changed now. They assume that our senses and mind are not the basis of reality, they protect against it.

Meditation keeps your mind with reality, and we can watch the things as it looks. Since you become more cautious, you feel that the whole sky is yours. I never suggested anyone be unselfish as I know that if you are selfish, then you will be unselfish spontaneously. When you are unselfish, then you are missing yourself; you cannot be in touch with anyone else if the original contact is missing. Neglect the all rules of your society and the world. Imagine that you are life's few years are left now. Now, you will start enjoying your life happily, no matter how you get it, whether you dance or sing, try to enjoy every moment of life because we know we are not immortal, with the spirit of your selfishness, the power of love will start flowing towards others. Now, we are able to share the love with others. Love is most selfish things in this world.

Love is free from all attachments

Love is the only liberty that is free from infatuation and attachment, as if you love everything in this universe, then you are not attached to anything in this world. Indeed, everyone has to understand the Phenomenon of attachment. It is not necessary to cling anything. For instance, you always think what's is available to us today; maybe this will not be available to us tomorrow. As you are afraid that you will lose it. It may be possible; someone cannot steal it. Nobody knows that what will happen tomorrow. Any person you love, whether he is a man or a woman – change in relationship is practical. You can become close friends and come closer, or the relationship can end because it does not always butterflies and rainbows.

When you meet someone at that time, the person can be a stranger. But after sometime, you will not be only yourself, and you can become a heart and two bodies. You can become one with each other and disappear in that bliss. The place of love has been left in the heart and love only. Love is great, beautiful, and uncontrollable that you cannot remain yourself and you have to lose yourself and disappear. In this disappearance, nobody supposed to attach. Once love bloom in its totality, the whole thing is simple. There is no fear of tomorrow because there is no question of marriage or attachment contract is generated. The meaning of love comprises freedom, which is free of all attachments. Whenever you are in love, it means that you are not attached to anything. Every moment arrives with new happenings, new majesty, and new music. Maybe the partner can change, but the love remains.

Love does not know about any attachment; love knows no probability of sinking from dignity and respect. Love is the honor of yourself; you can't act against it. It doesn't mean that you cannot change your partners. If the partners change, then the love lives in the same way as the river, which flows water to the sea, then in, reality, mankind will have more love than it has today. Love should not be confined to a person's thirst. Love requires to be oceanic; it is not a drop of a tap.

Love is never bound to any limit, and it is universal. It not only calls for some persons to celebrate, but it also reaches the whole existence whether it is a planet, sky, stars, forest, animals, and birds. Love is not dependent on something or is not limited to any area, and if you fall in love, then the whole existence is charming and lovable for you.

In my lifetime, I have never crossed a road which is against me. I have never seen such a river which flows opposite the sea. The entire world is adorable and delightful to me. As soon as you know about the blooming of love, all the questions regarding the attachment will end. If your partner exits from your life, it does not mean that it will never return to your life. It will not feel the bias towards him.

Humans should realize that they are like a child, playing in the park, collecting stone, playing with soil, and feeling happy in every moment of life that they have a big treasure have been found. If people start believing that they can find pleasure in little things of life, then keep himself in freedom and let others remain in freedom. This will turn the whole world into a new kind of existence.

However, if any lover says to his well-beloved that "You are the most beautiful girl in this whole world and I love you so much," if she never denied it does not mean that he has right to say such things if he does not know very well all women of the world. He completely forgets his irrationality.

When love becomes an attachment, then it turns into a relationship. If you are demanding in love, then it is a jail. In this way it destroys your freedom; you are not allowed to fly in the sky with full freedom, you are in the cage. I do not care about the people that what they will think about me when I usually alone in my room. Even, I do not care about others, if they are happy together in the room? But I'm comfortable in the room alone.

I know that in general, people in society are worried about unmarried. According to him, marriage is a universal law which should be followed indiscriminately.

Generally, people ask the same question "Why don't you marry a lovely girl?" Tortured by every person, one person chooses an option, it is better to marry. But after marriage they will not end the game, they will start asking the next question, "When will your child come?" Now, this is a big issue that is not in your hands. But, people will tease you "Without a child the house is quiet." The problems are not being solved, but continue to multiply. So, it's better not to bother anybody and sit in your room with your family or get busy in your work. I do not force people to get married and do not inquire about the birth of their child because these questions are not logical, it cannot be helpful, and the result may be an obstruction to freedom. People used to follow the same trend of married life, who wanted their lives with their wives and children. But, due to the less money or any other reason sometimes it will be disappointing. They are not using all their senses as you cannot bound the love for few persons or they do not know about all the consequences of married life. They are not aware of the simple rules of life, because when the lover falls in love, then you can see the glow on his face. You can check out the freshness in his walk just like a dance in it; you can see well-dressed clothes, and his heart in full of joy and every heartbeat is singing a song every moment. A beautiful thing has happened. But it does not last forever. After some months everything is same again, and boredom is settled; then you can check that the dust has stacked once again. The light has gone, dragging it again instead of the dance. Flowers are still fragrances, but you cannot feel this smell. The stars are shining in the sky, but you cannot see the sky. You know that few people can sleep with all the stars in the sky, with the feeling of greatness, vastness, and loneliness. Later people realized that if they were alone, it would have been better. Now nothing can be done. You cannot return once again back to your bachelor life. In fact, due to the uncertain truth, what will happen to you, if there is no member of your family then how you will help you in old age? I can say that this is a kind of agreement, so we like to be accustomed to prison that you cannot leave the jail. It is a kind of compromise or safety formula. Although, it is full of miserable.

Love gives the quality life with liberty; it gives you a new wing that helps to fly as much as high possible.

If love is not misunderstood in the form of lust, not only sexual desire or biological meeting of female and male hormones. Although it is considered a meeting of two souls, love becomes a great insight into your life and gives you high wings. And then only couples can always be friends. Otherwise, they will be like a hidden enemy.

Sex is a small quantum of biological energy. Love is the whole being, and it is your soul. Sex is a desire of the society to continue the human life cycle; if you want to participate, you can continue. When you try to avoid love at this moment, then all your creativity ends and senses become insensitive. Once again all dust start encompassing around you. You change to a zombie or living dead.

Every day, we follow the same routine of life that we sleep, eat, walk, talk, and go to our office until the end of life and boredom crawl on us for our whole life. We are only a robot or machine.

If you conceive love as a concrete and find love in this form of friendship in every person with such imagination, then you will not have to follow any religion or spirituality. Love flows towards the ultimate experience of happiness or Truth. If you give more importance to sex in your life, then nothing will be left to you. This means that you are trying to justify your lust and if you more think about the sense of enjoyment, then the more mind will become dissatisfied. Therefore, if you only consider sex and do not like to feel real love at all, then it means that you are going to lower or resort to low self-esteem, jealousy, and selfishness. These tasks can ultimately harm your life. You will never be aware of the beauty of reality, the real peace, and ecstasy of the cosmos. It sounds like you have become so famous and love can make it possible. So, don't forget, love not aware of boundaries. It cannot be jealous or hold. It is an absolute absurdity and unpleasant that you have someone because you love. If we possess anyone, that means you want to keep him as an object and kill someone's feelings because of your desire. Only commodities can be possessed. Love leads freedom. In fact, love is freedom.

Love and Health

Everyone knows the fact that relationship of love is good for health, if you have love in your life, then your mental health will be better because happiness makes us capable of experiencing life on excitement. Personal welfare is assessed on the basis of how well we are physically, mentally and socially.

Physical Health

We have a closer look at love then it is not all about the butterflies. There are so many chemical processes in the brain that affect us. When you first fall in love, the body releases hormones like dopamine and oxytocin. It rewards the sense of activeness, joy, faith, and trust. You feel immensely positive, encouraging and ravishing. Oxytocin hormones released when we begin to care or touch someone with the feeling of love. Some research suggests that oxytocin reduces stress, fear, and pain. It normalizes blood pressure, gives strength and boosts immunity power. As your love matures, the level of dopamine hormone can be high, but hormones like serotonin and cortisol help you calm down and settle the relationship without losing the mood.

Love and health go hand in hand, people are not aware of the harmful effects due to the feeling of hatred, envy, and revenge in their lives, which can create risk for health issues like heart problem, increase depression, high blood pressure and weakened immunity.

Mental Health

Love improves mental health in vigilance, knowledge, and creativity. It keeps a smile on your face. Love helps peoples to maintain close relationships with self-discoveries. We create relationships, improve our communication, you can manage our emotions in fruitful ways. It enhances our capacity to think, skills, and develop resilience. Humans are not perfect. Due to irritation and frustration, we hurt each other's feelings. We trapped by the perceptions and expectations, let each other go down. Although, some people successfully build long-term relationships, holding the hand of forgiveness, kindness, and acceptance. Researchers indicate that mindfulness contributes to improving our breathing system, more healthy life with longevity. It mitigates anxiety.

Social Health

If you believe in developing strong relationships and social skills, then there is the ability to show care and concern for others. Such access to skills improve our connections and relationships with others and enhances the power of conversation in the workplace. For relationships, we need to develop specialized skills to be helpful in fixing the issues without interrupting the privacy of others and manage the conflict without harming all connections.

When people feel attached with love and safety, their stress reduces and feeling close to another person can mitigate anxiety. We need a society of people to love. It ensures wellness in all areas of our lives and provides a slope of good boundary management for healthy connection. The hormone Oxytocin increases our capability to recognize, respond to a social signal, and improve all facets of well-being. But, loneliness may hurt our wellness and activate pain centers. It can stimulate anxiety, which can be observed by neurotransmitters and others hormones like adrenaline or cortisol increase levels. When someone feels insecurity, and this causes stress response of your body. Being in love and enjoying the company of another person can reduce the fear of depression and anxiety.

The presence of partner greets us with positive energy and accountability for ourselves, a condition for a successful connection.

"If you can look at everything lovingly, the whole world becomes beautiful. You realize love is not something that you can do."-- Sadhguru

"Love is the 7th sense that destroy all the 6 sense and makes the person non sense." -- Aqsayyed

'I'm loving every moment with you.'

Chapter - 9

Dance reach innermost & improve your Fitness

Dance is a delightful one, improve our fitness, and encouraging physical movement. A Lot of people concede in their daily routines, behavior, and lifestyle.

Physical activities are the necessity of life, and it should approach those people who are not active in their lives. Dance reach up to innermost areas of a person's heart and mind. Even, it reaches where language and words fail. Dance is the most lucid and expressive of anything else. You do not need the help of any language or are not specific to any society, or there is no need for sophistication to understand it. It is an expressive language which can be understood everywhere in this universe. The humans know very well about this language.

I can see the magnificent dancing of billions of stars like moon and sun rhythmically in the infinite sky; you cannot call it an ordinary dance. This show is not a business, and the purpose is not to entertain. If you believe it, then it should be known as mighty ecstasy.

One person needed dance for him, not only as he born with this ability. You can move your body and can learn dance. It is not so severe because you have to be alone in it. Love is quite tough as it requires a companion to dance with someone else. Nobody can reject you. Do not try to deny the dance and this is the great song of life. There are many ways of dance; you can pick it from its basket with your fascination. The famous styles of dancing comprise –

Indian classical and traditional dances

Bharatanatyam - Bharatanatyam is a solo dance technique, originated in South of India in Tamil Nadu. This dance is performed mostly by women, and it explains the endless understanding of spiritual thoughts based on body, mind, and soul.

Kathakali – This dance is one of the classical forms of dance originates from Kerala which located in south India. It is an expressive dance associated with storytelling art and evolved from several religious and social theatrical forms.

Manipuri – Manipuri dance is one of the primary forms of *Indian Art,* or c*lassical Dances* originated in the Manipur state in the northeast part of India. This dance related to traditional and ritual festivals.

Bhangra - Bhangra Dance is one of the traditional dances, which started in Indian from Punjab, is accompanying Dhol beat and it is a vibrant form of folk dance and people perform this dance while celebrating the harvest.

Western Dances

- **Salsa Dance** – This is partner dance and focuses on cadence, melody, and sensuality. It is comprising a blend of American and African efficacy.
- **Ballroom dance** – This dance requires many dancing partners and more famous in the public of the U.S and Europe.
- **Hip-hop Dance** – It usually performs on hip-hop music, it specifies that primarily street dance can include style like locking, popping and breaking, etc.
- **Belly dancing** – It is the most fun way of dance style originated in the Middle East, Emphasis on the movement of hips.

The Indian classical dances are mainly gesture-based dance. These dances depicting the activities and use of all main organs and their meanings and how these movements can be used to describe a story. In India, our cultures are primarily focusing on the body, becoming a source of gesture, mudras or movements used are more extensive than the western dances. These classical dances originated from ancient times for the reason of worship of God or due to other benefits. The usage of jewelry, costume or makeup in Indian traditional dance is more exclusive and sophisticated as compared to western dance. Western dance becomes an expression of actions, the source of entertainment, mainly reflecting romance, showcase the talents of the performer, and give a chance of instant money which requires full of energy. Classical dances of India concentrate on worship and praising the God, story describing, and showing all kinds of emotions whether it is related to mind, body or spirit.

Nowadays, western dances becoming more popular in India. Under the influence of Western civilization, the new generation of India accepts it as a representative of each new age, and it offers more money to the artist and even requires it for networking of social life. In major cities of India, you can see many discotheques are entirely crowded and famous for its nightlife and people are crazy for it, and they remain open and busy until the local authorities allow.

Dance and health

Dance for wellness evolves a necessary part in the remedy, cure, and other health conditions. Dance is the best technique to remain fit and suitable for all kind of shape, figures, and ages of the person. It is necessary for your mental and physical health. The different dances involve different body gestures and movements.

It helps in improving the condition of your hearts, enhance the strength of muscles and bones, weight management, lessen the body age, its enhance mental functioning and intellectual powers like self-determination, self-respect, authentic self and communication and language skills.

All dances can be considered an exercise and reduce the risk of diseases, assist in the reduction of weight and bring mental relief.

Dance is a kind of physical activity which keep a person more agile and active. It is not less than other physical activities such as tennis, badminton, and football. It makes stronger bones, even in the old age person can walk briskly.

Dance helps in controlling levels of total blood cholesterol. Dancing cut high cholesterol and maintain a ratio of "Bad" and "Good" Cholesterol. It improves your heart rate and blood pumping which other body part needed. Dance increase energy, improve sleep and balances overall body posture, which reduces back pain and focuses on facial expression and hand gestures. The efficiency of employees of government and private sector or businessman can be related to the benefits of dance for health.

Mental health

Dancing always positively impacts a person's mental health. Even I suggest that if couples want to live happily married life and want to save their marriage, they should learn to dance. It can change almost everyone. I have seen that the dance couple has wholly lost themselves in the movement in their arms. It is the best way to connect your body to music, mind, soul, and other people. Dance activity improves memory and troubleshooting techniques compared to other sports. It retouches the symptoms of dementia and treats dementia, even the regular dance also increased in cognitive acuity of all individuals. It helps in developing new neural connections that connects our neuronal synapses.

Nowadays, Psychiatrists are recommending Dance therapy to treat their patients with mental stress as dance helps in connecting you with the inner self. Even the employees have to face the workplace stress in the offices due to the uncertainty of the burden of work and indulge in workplace politics to gain appraisement from senior and tainting the reputation of the companion which causes the psychological distress. But, companies like Google, Microsoft, Facebook providing an outstanding environment and other perk and advantages like they don't need to leave the workplace for recreational activities like painting, physical workout, dancing, etc.

The number of studies showing dancing is one of the healthy exercises. Its aims to increase performance and improve welfare and health efforts. Dance does not need a high level of interpersonal skills, and yet it seems that it is a powerful indicator of fitness because it reflects developmental strength and stability. Dancing can be the best way to stay fit for people of all ages, shapes, and sizes.

'I let my life dance on the edge of time to stay.'
conscious and happy.'

Chapter - 10

Music - Fuel for the soul

The Oxford dictionary meaning of music as "the art of combining vocal or instrumental sounds (or both) to produce beauty of form, harmony, and expression of emotion."

Music is a fusion of sounds generated by various kinds of musical instruments, makes it is pleasant and desirable for our mind and ears. It pertains to whatsoever that has a soothing sound. Its melodies designed to leave a significant influence and create great happiness. Its efficacy and divinity is like a blessing and works as nourishment for our soul. I can see the existence of music all over. I can sense whistles in blowing winds. I can feel music in raindrops. I can always be enticing with waves of an ocean. Even, murmuring of the leaves creating a paradise environment. Indeed, music takes away the boredom of our lives. Music is an ecstasy that is admired by all. There are various facades of music; it can be divided into several categories depending on tone, melody, rhythm and few of the famous music are:

Jazz Music - Jazz is the best and innovative one in my opinion, and it is yet fresh like a hundred years ago. Southern America's original music art genre. It created specifically from blues and ragtime. It portrayed by syncopated rhythms, harmonious playing, modifying degrees of improvisation, and deliberately distortions of timbre and pitch.

Hip-Hop Music - Hip-Hop is famous music which originated in the United States in New York by inner-city Africans-American during the 1970s. Its elements are styling rhymes over a beat covers with rapping.

Rock and Roll Music - This is the 1950s primarily music of dance that evolved in the United States. Its powerful beats and tunes are appreciated. It has developed from the composition of music like jazz, country music, and blues music. It's beat obtained from a blues boogie beat. It's characterized by a drum beat that is ordinarily 4/4 riffs created by drums, vocals, and guitars.

Blues Music – This music is developed by the fusion of Western and African cultures, originated in the Southern region of America. It consists of bass lines, lyrics, and instrumentation and many types of music. A musician with guitar usually sings it. This music style is related to feeling and emotions like love, sensuality, drinking, job, and luck.

Country Music - Country music originated in the Southern U.S in the 1930s. It is a blend of style tracing its roots in dance tunes, and ballads played especially on guitar, banjo, and fiddle. It evolved by a different form of music like blues, Celtic music, gospel music, traditional folk music. This music usually developed around three chords with a usual melody.

Pop Music – Pop music is a form of popular music that originated in U.S and U.K during the 1950s. It is improvised through its song made up of repeated chorus and poetry. This music connected with rock and roll and rock styles.

Folk Music - The word folk music used for modern popular music which based on the traditions. It uses guitars type instruments instead of traditional instruments. This music is powerful and usually given a gifted from one generation to another. Most of the tunes related to the unknown original writer. When passing through generations it goes by some modifications, and memorable part becomes stronger.

Indian Classical Music

Indian Classical Music has been sustaining its existence for centuries. It has fascinated the whole world. It has divinity, and astonishing strength helps you to follow the path of God.

In ancient times, Indians were influenced by spiritual power, and this led to the rise of Indian classical music. Thus, whosoever understand it deeply; then it is a rewarding experience that includes single-minded devotion and life-long commitment.

Usually, music involves mainly three elements like rhythm, melody, and harmony. Since it is spiritual, the Indian classical music in north India focuses primarily on melodic development. Even rhythm plays a significant role, which giving texture and a sense of purpose to a melody. Harmony takes in the form of a harmonic resonance field used by some instruments like the tanpura/ swarmandal/santoor and the harmonium and the tabla attach the 3rd dimension of harmony.

One of the favorite things of Indian classical music, if you have learned the basic notes, and introduced to ragas (musical themes), and then you are promoted to start making your melodies. Indian classical music is a particular genre of two traditions - the traditional music of North Indian area of India is known as Hindustani classical music, and the traditional expression of music from South Indian music termed as Carnatic.

Indian classical music consists of two elements: - Raga and Tala.

Raga provides an artist with the fabric of a melodic structure to build melody from sound.

Tala gives the framework for rhythmic improvisation using time cycle. In several types of researches, it was found that Indian classical music enhances mood and concentration on their work.

However, western modern music is getting very popular nowadays. People are more attracted to its significant money proposals and but it mainly focuses on sensuality. In the west the modern music has fallen so much, In reality, it comes close to the sex and destroying almost purity of music. If music is used to stimulate lust and sexuality, then naturally it falls into that category.

Music and Spirituality

Music is a language which is quite near to peace, the sound of music which can make the soundless. Music is nothing like physiology or study topic on chemistry or physics, and yet it is one of the deepest and miraculous things. If we only consider it on intellectual terms, then it is not possible because I think it is beyond the mind. Although, it still not concretely meditation. Music is somewhere between contemplation and mind.

In ancient times, the mediators could not find a path to convey their feeling, in this way most of the traditional music is comes out of meditation. Human's converted the sounds into meaning. Natural sounds have no purpose in itself. There is a kind of noise in the wind blowing from the tree, therein music itself or just like that downfall of the river from the mountain through stones has music its own. The usual idea of music is that there are sounds in it, this is the only half-truth. Although, when the music gets comes closer and more profound, it dwells of silence between the two sounds. There is a famous proverb in China "When the musician became perfect; then he throws away his instruments" as they can generate noise only. At the perfection level, a musician or a mediator can create silence. It is weird, but it refers to every mastership. An archer becomes perfect; and then he throws his arrows and bow. He can fall down the bird by only blinking of his eyes. Arrows and Bow are just a beginner's practice level. I think the music should bring inner dance, inner silence, and people like it.

I listen to blessed music, but I don't want to look at your musical instruments. The music referred to the whole existence, and the device applies to you. I am only a way to reach this music, and in this way, I don't want to see any instrument, and I want to look at myself. Who am I? For whom I am playing music? I only want to hear my silence. I am embracing specific music. This music exists in my love, faith, peace, and trust. In intense love, synchronicity happens. When you start doing things with your depth; then you will not need any instrument like piano, guitar, and saxophone. But don't consider that your music, songs, and dance have no worth. They specifically belong to the most significant value, whereas they don't deserve any price. Music is your innovation. But we have lost contact with authentic music.

Listening to music is the key to good health

Music influences mental and physical health of a person. Listening to music is a fantastic feeling that improves concentration power, provides relaxation, and mitigate anxiety. Different psychologists believe that music creates a friendly environment. It's accepted in scientific studies that plants and livestock acknowledge positively to music. For instance, Buffalo produces more milk each day while listening to music. Elephants and birds are the best singers can make music like human beings. Continuous listening music runs camels and horses in a more controlled manner. Goldfish can be trained to differentiate between the musicians. Even, crops give better yields regarding both quantitatively and qualitatively.

Psychologists suggest music therapy because it is the safest treatment which not only cures, satisfies patients permanently. The right kind of music when appropriately used, effects on:

1. **Improves workout** - During exercising music provides you a better workout and results. It will enhance your overall power, elevates your mood and distracts from uneasiness or discomfort during your workout.
2. **Quick recovery** - Listening to music during illness keeps body recovery fast. Slow music provides better relaxation and helps in the fast physical recovery process.
3. **Memory loss** - Many people suffer from memory loss problems. It affects a person's daily life to a great extent. Music helps the patient to memorize songs and tune and improves memory to get connected with their experiences. It is possible because the music reaches that part of the brain that is next to memory.

4. **Music impact on metabolism rate** - It accelerates the rate of metabolism and improve the digestion power. Music boosts the regulation of the sympathetic nervous system and the hypothalamic-pituitary axis which is essential in the regulation of metabolism and energy balance.
5. **Increase endurance and helps in controlling pain** - Listening to music boost the physical performance and endurance power of the body. It works through simply distraction of the mind as you are listening to your favorite music album, even you can't notice that you walk and cover an extra distance. It affects the internal excretions and secretions, improves muscular activities and boosts overall immunity system. It assists in reducing the intensity of pain, focuses on relieving, and preventing the patient's suffering.
6. **Reduce mental stress and boost the function of the blood vessel** - Listening to music can reduce your stress by triggering biochemical stress reducers, and patients feel a healthy effect on blood vessel function. Music keeps the patient happier and increases the flow of blood in their blood vessels.
7. **Inspire attention** - Listening instrumental music and different brainwave music like Mozart classical and meditative sounds can increase your concentration power; techno and heavy metal techno release your mind from depressive symptoms. Using rhythmic music, can helps you to ease symptoms of migraines and behavioral issues. If we are feeling low in, then music helps you to pick you up.
8. **Elevate mood** - Music always puts you in a better mood and helps you to understand your feelings. Even people like to listen to music while driving which keep relaxing their mind.

Improve overall health system

Music is capable of many health benefits like

- It improves respiration organs, strengthens your lungs and affects the whole respiratory system.

- Pure rhythmic music helps you in the recovery of cases like stammering and lisping.
- It impacts on speech and develops vocal hearing coordination.
- It has a direct effect on the nervous and circulatory systems.
- Music is a significant health tool to reduce many types of physical disorders and to lower down stress levels, increase consciousness, evolving mind in meditation that has a higher result of health benefits.

I believe music is the expression of humanity and all of us have touched it. Music is itself is a treatment that heals the soul, and it doesn't differentiate between cultures, *everybody loves music.*

"Most beautiful music in the world is your heartbeat. It plays in rhythm even when the world leaves you alone."

'I'm enjoying the music passion itself.'

Chapter - 11

Aura and Chakra affects our health

Everything is made of energy. Everything goes to emit energy in this universe in various forms. Human bodies are associated with different types of energy. One from which we call the human aura, it is a bioenergy field made up of various colors and layers. All humans have a visible body; even they have another invisible body called Human Aura or Human energy field. Everyone doesn't have an awareness of this fact. Maybe you agree or not agree to this. Let's try to understand this. If you ever experience that just because of the presence of the person we feel sad or glad or terrible. An Enlighted person is associated with a large human Aura; if he comes close to you well, then you will feel attracted. When your ego is dissolved, then you are entirely connected to wholeness. But, if there is ego, then you will never be connected to fullness, and there will be constant conflicts and struggle in your life, and your energy begins flowing out. It reduces the size of your aura, and you will lose your freedom and feel more unconscious.

Aura layers

All energy healers believe that every human being has a flow of energy (Aura) around a body. The human aura depicts information connected with the Astral, emotional, mental, spiritual, and physical body. It can tell about the health conditions of your body.

The human aura is believed to be made of seven different layers of colors of energy that are all interconnected.

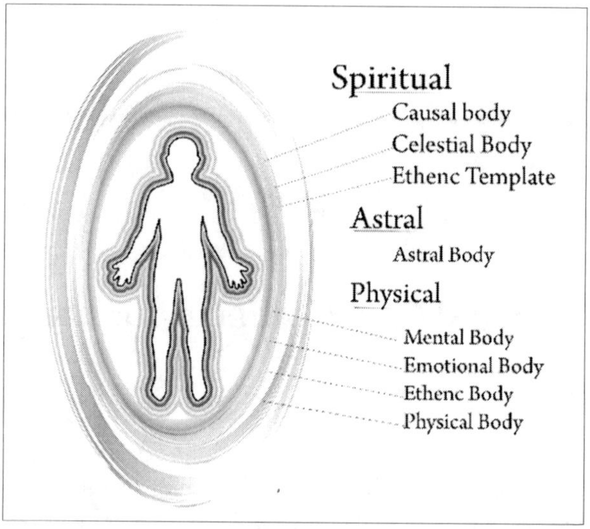

Fig 11.0

Layer 1 - The first layer or Etheric layer represents state between energy and matter. It is red and related to Root or Muladhara Chakra. It seems like a physical body and similar in size and dimensions. It holds the link with health, and responsible for vibrations, creative energy, and vital energy. It maintains physical needs and acts as a vehicle through cosmic energy our energy systems are translated. It helps to generate hunger, thirst, heat, cold, and dream. The outcome of contrary belief on the Body are Physical illness, Pain, Complication.

Layer 2 - Emotional Layer is connected to the emotions, inner feeling vibration levels, and elemental body. It is orange in color related with Second chakra Sacral or Swadisthana. Anger, worry, sorrow, afraid are primarily concern with negative Belief. The impact of contrary belief on the body are Dark blocks and depleted energy. When this layer has blockages, then you have to fight with your feeling and emotions, even with sexuality.

Layer 3 – This layer is associated with the mental body, which is linked to mental processes and vibrational level of thoughts. It is yellow and related to Manipura or solar plexus Chakra. The adverse outcomes of mental body are an unwanted idea, negative emotions, and beliefs. To balance it we need a logical mind, with basic instinct and sharp intellect.

Layer 4 – This layer center of transformation and transition associated with the processes and functional energies of life in the physical world. The astral body is related to Anahata or heart Chakra and emits a green hue. It indicates the division between the spiritual and physical layers. The effect of negative perception in the body is heaviness on the chest and stagnated energy. The layer is essential for overall health status. To keep the layer in balance, you can choose Meditation techniques and Reiki treatment therapies.

Layer 5 - Etheric body layer forms exist in an empty or negative space that creates the structured energy field through which your physical body grows. It is blue and attached to the throat or Vishuddha Chakra where managing of sounds and voice creates matters. If there is any contrary belief on the layer and to balance it, internal recognition and specificity sensitivity is needed and provide a commitment to follow and speaks the truth.

Layer 6 - Celestial Body associated with the third eye chakra and has an indigo color. This is the hub through which we feel blissful states of unconditional love and self-consciousness. At this Centre point, we recall our oneness and get connected to all existence. It is associated with the influences of self-awareness and Intuitive level where we enter to higher spirituality and intelligence.

Layer 7 – Ketheric or Casual body is associated with Divine consciousness and linked to Crown (Sahasrara) Chakra, and it emits a violet hue. It includes the impressions related to the events of a person's past life events which our soul has ever experienced within their present body incarnation. It *Is the purest form, and It makes a link to God,* understand the universal paradigm. This layer cannot be experienced from the limited point of your ego.

Aura and Health analysis

Aura photography helps like:-

I. To examine the worse outcome of electromagnetic radiations of various electronic devices like mobile phones on health.

II. To understand the future and present of health issues of the full body.

III. To check the positive or negative results of emotions and yogic exercise.

IV. The healer can check the energy of room after group meditation and get reports after treatment of the patient.

V. It indicates clues to the patient's Variation in shapes, colors, and intensity images are said to overall health and energy level.

VI. Even Researchers or Physicians also recommend Aura Image. It plays a role in identifying perilous diseases like Cancer and heart attack. For instance, Cancerous plants appear with a very vivid corona or electric field compared to healthy plants. It is because of the excessive metabolic rate of cancer cells.

VII. Kirlian photography uses the process of electrical discharges or Aura Images to treat its patients. These images show the emotional status of the patients.

VIII. *In Acupuncture* treatments, Aura Photography can consider during an initial inspection where the energy is out of balance.

Aura therapy helps to balance hormone, clear out unessential energy, and revive your life with a sense of power which increases the energy field through expanding love. It improves the person's overall state of mind and body, wherever you go.

Understanding about "Chakras" or "Circle."

There are seven major energy centers or Human Chakras in our body. These "Chakra" or "Circle" is an expression of constant spin movement, gives us life energy to flow in and out of Aura. These energy Chakras are positioned or embedded from one dimension to another and beginning with the backbone or spinal column, extend to the crown of the head. Every chakra is believed to vibrate at a various level of the frequency generating multiple colors, and their prime role is to make our physical body nourish and helps in creating awareness for the evolvement of our consciousness.

These "Chakras" are related to both mental and physical health. The aligned "Chakras" reflects that the person is living a peaceful, relaxed and healthy life and he is enjoying easy going life. Every time our energy field varies depending on the state of mind. Good habits, Positive thinking and eating a healthy diet keeps our "Chakras" spinning properly. These "Chakras" are associated with our wellness, and if any of the "Circle" becomes weak, then organ connected to particular Chakra becomes unhealthy too. The aura or human energy field has a strong link with our nervous system create harmony between our mind, body, and soul. An individual's thoughts, feelings, idea, and beliefs are reflected in the human energy field that is why the Aura and Chakras can detect critical issues associated with physical traits.

Now, Modern Science states that human physical structure is not only made of molecules but also made up of human energy fields. The Enlighted Persons had recognized this process in the past. "Aura" and "Chakras" are now common terms that surround and penetrate the physical body. The human Chakras are a powerful matrix which includes the mental, physical, and spiritual facets of self.

In the modern era, a number of instrument have been developed to see the positive or negative energies (invisible electromagnetic filed) associated with Aura such as Aura Scanner, Aura Bio-well camera, GDV Dowsing tool, Aura video station, IES Aura Cloud, Lecher Antenna, which can examine human psychology, behavior, energy releases and healing required body parts can be observed.

Seven charkas and its effects is:

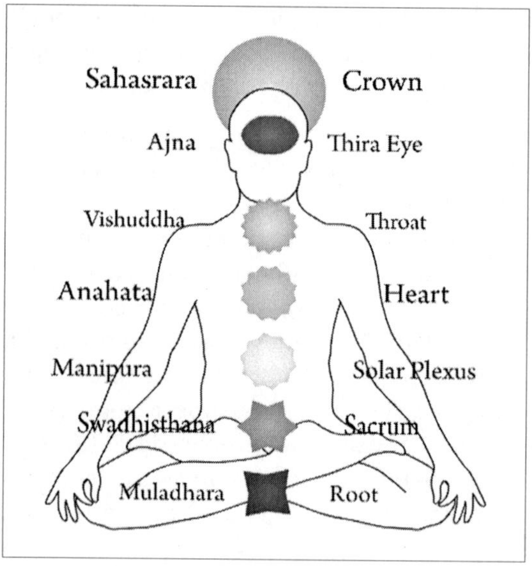

Fig 11.1

First Chakra – "Root Chakra" or "Muladhara"

The "Muladhara Chakra" is a beginning point of our spiritual development. It located in the lowest point of our spinal column, in the coccyx area. The color used to represent this chakra is Red. It governs our reproductive organs and responsible for feelings of fear, passion, intimacy, etc. If Muladhara chakra becomes off balance, at this time body revolts and more inclined to toward the feelings of insecurity, fear, and meaningless sex. A person can experience anxiety, fears, or nightmares. This fear and insecurity give rise to diseases like Eating disorders, constipation, prostate cancer, sexual dysfunction, and restlessness can be an indication of a 'Root Chakra' imbalance.

If your energy is more active in 'root chakra,' then you will be craving for more food and sleep in your life.

Ways to heal 'Root Chakras'

- Meditation is the best way for you to heal the 'Muladhara chakra.'
- Creating a harmonious relationship with your surroundings and environment play an essential role in enhancing safety.
- By strengthening your belief, helps you in creating a comfort zone that is a healthy adaptation.
- Add Fibrous, and Natural Foods in your diet will improve the chakra functioning.

When your Root chakra is balanced, you will feel a sense of calmness and richness in your life.

Second chakra – "Sacral Chakra" – "Svadhishana"

The "Sacral Chakra" is associated with Orange color and located in the lower belly. This chakra represents the creative spirit to enjoy life, teaches us to love ourselves before we love others and maintain healthy interpersonal relationships.

This chakra which translates your identification as a human and what to do with it.

You are feeling that you are enjoying the things that are not nourishing for your soul or are not healthy for you, then your second chakra is out of balance. It can contribute to symptoms like obesity, addiction, hormone imbalances, low blood sugar, lower back pain, depression.

If your energy is more dominant in sacral chakra, you will be involved in more pleasant activities. You will like to enjoy material pleasure and the physical world differently.

There are many ways, as you can do to balance it:

- Consider talking with a close friend and your loved ones that are bothering you.

- Dance is another way to heal this Chakra which removes blockages and keeps your body is getting energy flowing.
- To improve the Sacral Chakra, you can try various Yoga-Poses like Half frog pose, Open-angle pose, and Fire log pose.
- Keep your hand in front of Sacral chakra and imagine yourself that rays are coming from hand to heal your chakra. After a few days, you will feel you relax and cool.
- Healing stones and crystals for our cleansing of chakra is the most common measure.

Third chakra – Solar Plexus – Manipura

The "Solar Plexus" starts above your navel and extends up to the sternum. This is a source of self-esteem, self-confidence, willpower and personal power.

"Manipura" is the Sanskrit word for "Solar Plexus." It is explained as "shining gem," and represented as being a golden yellow in color. The Manipura is just like a sun's warm glowing rays, it lights up your way and warms your body with the glow of self-mastery that empowered you to master your emotions and thoughts.

If your "Manipur chakra" is blocked, it may affect the digestive system or even unbalances your organs like liver, kidney, and pancreas. Persistently you may face frustration and disappointments. It settles for lack of self-confidence and self-determination. It may be a result in criticism, and you may feel that your opinion, words, and efforts are not appreciated.

Healing of Solar Plexus Chakra

- It is recommended to wear yellow colored clothes or spend some time in the sunshine to stimulate this Chakra.
- Crystals and Gems and like amber, Topaz, and yellow Citrine can help to balance the Third Chakra.
- The yellow color is associated with Manipura Chakra, which means that sunflower seeds, bananas, yellow peppers, etc. are good for healing of Third Chakra - Solar plexus.

- Regular practice yoga of poses like Warrior Pose, Boat Pose, Sun salutations is ideal for chakra balancing.

Well balanced Third chakra can effectively assist you in achieving life goals and Objective. You become an achiever; you can easily do many things in the world successfully.

Fourth chakra – Heart – Anahata

The "Heart Chakra" is located in the center of the chest. It is extended down to your breastbone and up to your throat. Green Color represents the Heart Chakra, and it is connected with love, joy, compassion, caring, inner peace and kindness. Heart Chakra is a unifying chakra, bringing absoluteness of love, love for yourself and love for others.

An imbalanced Anahata may result in a lack of love and compassion, and it can influence our happiness and relationships. A blocked heart chakra may lead to symptoms like heart troubles, poor circulation, and respiratory illness.

Healing of Fourth Chakra

- The heart chakra is related to Air, and with the breathing exercises you can balance your energy;
- Develop your appreciation for beauty, include people, Art, and nature.
- Regular meditation and yoga practice like Bikram Yoga is beneficial for healing of this Chakra.
- Just by opening up of your hearts or love to others is the best way of healing exercise. It connects with our true essence and soul.
- Balance your food diet with Green colored foods like Leafy Vegetables, Kiwi, Apple and spinach Green tea, Garlic, and Cocoa.

If your energy is more effective in 'heart chakra,' you are a creative and innovative person. A person who is creative such as singer, artist or actor, is a person who spread that compassion to people around him.

Balanced and robust heart chakra helps you to live independently from anger and fear in your daily lives. Take a deep breath and imagine that green light is coming into your body and cleansing it, you are filled with deep love. With Regular practice, helps you to avoid falling in negative emotions and you will be inclined towards the place of compassion more.

Fifth Chakra - Throat - Vishuddha

The fifth Chakra is "Throat chakra" also called as Vishuddha in the Hindu tradition. It is positioned on the throat base and associated with blue color which symbolizes communication, self-expression, and expression of truth and creativity. This Chakra controls all areas of the throat, mouth, jaw, and thyroid gland.

The 5th chakra is considered to very pure and even as the seat of the emotional hub. If you are emotionally upset, then you often 'choked up' and unable to speak clearly and responsible for the flow and regulation of hormones.

Our 5th chakra becomes imbalanced, the effect manifested in different ways of symptoms a sore throat, hoarseness, thyroid problems, neck pain, throat pain, frequent infections, cavities, mouth ulcers or may suffer from a loud voice.

To Heal the Throat Chakra:

- The best way of healing is yoga asana and meditation. Sit in a comfortable position and start breathing as every breath enters through the nose and then passes behind the throat and into the lungs. Now, exhale this breath slowly out from the mouth, so try to alert yourself to listen to the sound of "hum" is related to the air that leaves your body. Repeat this chant enjoy the clear sound of your voice forever.
- You can use Sodalite, Turquoise, Aquamarine, Angelite are some effective and powerful crystals for the healing of throat chakra.
- Make healthier food choices such as soups, fruits that lubricate the throat is best for the Vishuddha Chakra.

- You can have a positive belief that "I speak freely and with confidence. It is now safe for me to express my feelings and to create the life I desire."

When your throat chakra is balanced, you can express yourself well, especially in a verbal manner. It assists you to live a life full of authenticity, and you don't need to worry about criticism and judgment from others.

If your energy is more active in 'Throat Chakra,' you will be an influential person, but this power is not only related to administrative or public affairs. An individual can be robust and dominant in a different manner, he can manage things at one place, and acts will happen for him. He can reveal life beyond the boundaries of space and time.

Sixth Chakra – The Third Eye – Ajna

The Sixth Chakra is "Ajna" located in the center of the eyes, between your eyebrows. Indigo is the color of third eye chakra connect you "beyond wisdom" and is recognized as the entry point of intuition. Our ideas, dreams, goals, and our values all rooted from Ajna. It bridge between heaven and earth, life and death and brings clarity to the sense organs like hearing, watching, and feeling.

If your Ajna Chakra is not in balanced, then you may experience frequent headaches or allergies. It may also tend to unsympathetic or irrational in thinking. You may suffer delusionally and create a situation in your mind that things are not happening.

Ways to heal third eye chakra:

- Meditation, Physical exercise, and yoga poses stimulate the Sixth Chakra, which involves
  - Child's pose, Savasana, Shoulder Stand, and
  - Dropping down body forward;
  - Taking a walk, just lying on the earth;
  - Taking a bath and feel the soothing warm water around you.

- ➢ You can do practice on a daily basis with positive affirmation 'I am an intelligent decision maker;' 'I am open to the inner wisdom within;' 'I believe on my intuition.'
- ➢ You can try healing stones like quartz, lapis lazuli, moonstone, amethyst, etc.
- ➢ Consider Reiki Healing therapy, acupressure as aimed to enhance awareness towards authentic connection inside.

If your energy is active in the 'Third Eye Chakra,' then you become the spiritually enlightened person, and you have achieved peace and stability within yourself. The outside world does not bother you any more.

Seventh Chakra – Crown – Sahasrara

Violet is the "Crown Chakra" color also called as "Sahasrara" in Sanskrit. The Crown Chakra is located at the top of your head. It is linked to spirituality and helps you to connect with the energy of wholeness and ecstasy.

The Crown Chakra is pure consciousness energy and associated to our higher selves, that created life forms and all things in the universe. This chakra can brings mindfulness, spiritual insight, and inspires everyone to live with all aspects of life. If this chakra is blocked, it can affect all the other chakras, or it may cause physical illness and mental disorders. A blockage in the crown chakra can lead subtle, systemic problems like chronic fatigue, mental fog and depression, Migraines and other chronic headaches.

Ways to bring Crown Chakra healing:

- Spend most of your time in open spaces and understand that the vastness and beauty of nature is a part of you.
- Use healing stones and crystals like amethyst, celestite, clear quartz, obsidian, or blue sapphire.
- Commit yourself daily practice an affirmation. Examples include, 'I am an open and expanded being;' 'I am connected to the Divine Source.'
- Share your issue in front of great divine powers of the universe and keep the trust that aid is already reached.

- Meditate by envisaging a golden light around your head and feel this light is entering through Crown Chakra and rejuvenate and recharge your physical and spiritual bodies.

When it's balanced and open, you will sense enigmatic wholeness with every being and everything in this universe engrossed in ecstasy and calmness. There is no outer stirring; you are just ecstatic as your energy has touched a certain height. Balanced chakra can assist in the treatment of migraines and brain tumors as well.

Overview of Chakras

"Chakras" or "Energy centers" are encircled by an immense sense of mystery. The vital-force from the universe stimulates your 'energy circles' through the Crown Chakra, moves down through the other energy centers, then out from the Root Chakra.

These Energy centers are vibrating at a specific frequency and respond to different wavelengths of light. In these wavelengths and frequencies, each color includes information and facts on various levels like mental, physical, and spiritual. It already described in the Chapter that there is a bonding between different emotion and color.

When you place a piece of metal in front of the magnet, then you can sense and understand about the energy and attraction, but you are not able to see it. Consciousness energy is present everywhere and in everything. It connects us to the whole universe. However, it can't be possible, if there is less energy or too much energy in unhealthy chakras. Due to the imbalance energy centers, the possibility of diseases may increase. Unhealthy energy centers are similar to blocked arteries, indicates an obstruction in the functioning of the body.

If our energy centers are balanced, we will be healthy and strong. It is indeed our energy centers like the seed of cosmic energy as more than something personal or individual.

'I am happy to align and balance my chakras.'

Chapter - 12

Planet affects our lives

Every being is connected to planets and stars that revolve around it, and we are a part of it. We have a close affinity with the planets of our solar system.

Every planet depicts different terrain in our life, another part of the compass of life, which constitutes us from forces like (i) Gravity, (ii) Electromagnetic, (iii) Nuclear-weak, (iv) Nuclear-strong. The first two can affect things at a considerable distance from the atomic nucleus. Planets may have a direct impact on us, by way of one or both of those forces.

The first notion is "Ether (Aether) theory" is an opinion of physics, a proposed medium that was assigned to Electromagnetic waves that the hypothetical substance through which electromagnetic waves travel. There should be some level of substance on empty spaces that essential for electromagnetic and gravitational forces to work. We can observe the gravity working in orbit of our planet around the sun or a satellite surround the Earth that means there would be some level of substance which fills the emptiness. It explains how the forces move in the universe. Aristotle, Sir Isaac Newton, and others scientists convinced that the light of the stars reaching us on earth spreading slithery through a medium the known as 'luminiferous ether.' However, an experiment conducted by the U.S. Scientists Michelson and Morrey in the 19th century was first to disprove this 'Ether theory.' There is a possibility that 'luminiferous ether' actually subsists, but it is difficult to prove. But in 1920 Albert Einstein was accepting the ether theory and said "Recapitulating, we may say that according to the general theory of relativity space is endowed with physical qualities; in this sense, therefore, there exists an ether. According to the general theory of relativity space without ether is unthinkable; for in such space there not only would be no propagation of light, but also no possibility of existence for standards of space and time ..."

The second consideration is related to 'Electric Universe theory' that represents the significance of electricity throughout the cosmos. While research has revealed that it is based on the recognition of existing natural electrically charged field phenomena, which is known as properties of plasmas or ionized gases. It makes up the visible universe and strongly responds to electromagnetic fields. The electric currents stream flow through plasma filament's shape and power galaxies. The currents stream flows into stars, powering them like fluorescent bulbs.

Five Elements and its effect on health

Almost every living being in this nature is composed of 5 basic elements in different volumes in a balanced manner. Water (Blood), Air (Breath), Fire (Heat), Earth (Bones and Muscles), and Space (Emptiness within). These elements are described as "Panchbhutas" in Sanskrit.

Largely it is water, **72%** is water. Another **12%** is earth. The next **6%** is air, and **4%** is fire. The remaining **6%** is space. If we sync it in the context of our planet; approximately 72% of the planet is water. In this way only, life is evolved. Thus, nearly 2/3rd of the planet is water; likewise, 2/3rd of the body is water. These elements are the foundation of our creation. Every element is responsible for various structures in the body.

- Earth constitutes our solid structures like flesh, bones, tissues, skin, and hair. Smooth muscles help break the food.
- Water forms anything that is liquid including blood, urine, saliva, urine, semen, and sweat. Digestive juices to help digest food.

- Fire is responsible for hunger, sleep, thirst, love, and affairs of the heart. It is a spark inside that helps to digest food.
- Air is anything that is a gas, and it is the easiest one as there is breath and easy to manage in a certain way. Air is responsible for all movement, such as contraction, expansion, and suppression.
- Space is the mother of other elements. The wisdom of space as a bright emptiness is the foundation of supreme spiritual knowledge. Space forms repulsion, physical attraction and, as well as fear.

Even, the whole system of ancient cultures was treating these elements. Stones, Crystals, Metals, as well as Sky, Air, Water, Fire, Ourselves, Planets, Stars, and Universe all comprises energy. This energy, allows every being in this Cosmos to make it function.

If any one element is taken out, the body will stop functioning. Some energy is necessary for life like biological energy, chemical energy, electrical energy, magnetic energy, mechanical energy. This energy drives the body. These are known as Life energy or Vital force. Even, an imbalance in the 5 elements brings imbalance in the Life Energy. If any of the five elements is out of balance or impure, then it will result in health issues and disease.

I. Out of balance of Fire element - If the fire element becomes weakens in a person. One may suffer

- Acidity, Fever, Coldness, Diabetes;
- Skin diseases, Increase Heat in the body;
- Digestive diseases, Vital energy loss;
- Insomnia, and Mental disorders.

  Hatha Yoga can increase the digestive fire to such an extent that they can remove gastrointestinal disorders. The anger and the anxiety usually bring up it more. The best technique to keep this fire is switching. Gradually, to stabilize yourself, you need to switch consciously between your logical left brain (rationale processing, analytic, objective) and your right brain (Govern's emotions, intuitions, creativity, Imagination). Work out, Meditation, Playing with music instrument are some of the ways that help you to switch.

II. Out of balance of Air element - It can lead to the problem of

- Nervous disorders, blood pressure problems;
- Lung disorders, Physical Pains;
- Depression, Locomotors Ataxia, etc.

Try to focus on your breath during asana. By including Yoga techniques like Pranayama practice in your daily routine that enhance your inner strength and it can help you to rebalance it.

III. Out of balance of Water element - Sufferings may occur such as

- Asthma, Sinusitis, Frequent Cold, Fatigue easily and Swellings;
- Dry Skin or Eyes;
- High blood pressure, Blood-thinning or Blood clotting;
- The problem of urination; Bladder infections and Diseases of Reproductive organs.

Do not drink excessive water or less water. When you feel thirsty, drink as much plain water as you need it. Regular physical exercise can help to Detoxify and improve blood circulation. Eat blue, purple foods. Avoid added sugars.

IV. Out of balance of Earth element - This can leave the individuals in ailments like

- Weakness, Obesity, cholesterol;
- Weight loss and Weight gain;
- Bones or Muscular Diseases, etc.

Choose zero-calorie foods and fruits like Watermelon, Raspberry, and salad like Cucumber, Lemon, etc. Practice mindfulness of breath and walk on the ground, soil, and grass on barefoot. However, you could not follow your regular diet timetable and failed to lose weight. Do not worry, when you actually feel hungry, eat natural foods. During the meal, thanks to the earth, from which this food comes.

V. Out of balance of Space element - It can cause diseases such as

- Thyroid disorders, throat problems;
- Speech disorders, epilepsy, ear diseases;
- Madness and foolishness.

For quick fix solutions use Reiki Healing therapy. You can emphasize the yoga poses and the series of meditation. You can repeat the positive affirmation "I love and accept myself in every situation of life."

Get Acupressure and Acupuncture treatments to clear blockages and restore right energy flow between the body organs. Yoga exercises help in the cleanliness these elements, improve health and balance, it unzips the inner strength involved in each element.

If you find success in purifying these elements, you will lead an incredible life. If you forget the living a lustrous life and you transcend the life (Meaning of Transcending - you are beyond it) because stunning life is a more complicated situation than transcending. What is beyond is not affected by several complexities of the physicality. But if you don't have mastery over the physical, you will only be slaves of your physicality. Everyone in this nature has many capabilities with these elements. Otherwise, you will not be able to live a normal life.

Knowing of these elements let you believe the natural laws and adapt yoga to obtain better physical fitness, overall health, strength, intellect, wisdom, and ecstasy. Currently, how better you are organized with these 5 elements, determines how stable and robust this body is.

Connection with one another the Elements

All 5 elements have a specific connection with the one other element; it depends on their nature. These connections set the laws of nature. Few elements are contradictory, each of which interrupts one another's expression. For instance, if they meet eventually, water and fire can attack each other. Need to be separate to keep fire and water in coexistence. Excessive fire in the body will tend to inflammation, but excessive water may dampen the fire and results in indigestion. The relationship between Fire and Air is that they increase each other.

The relationship between other elements is merely supportive, friendly and cooperative with each other. For example, the relationship between Earth and Water is said to "love" each other as both are supportive of each other. Air and Water can stay together without any issue, as in soda water. The same happens with fire and earth.

Significance of 5 fingers

The 5 Fingers are a manifestation of the Life energy or Vital Force. Most of the energy flows through the fingers. These fingers show various elements of the Vital force.

1. **Little finger** - Water [Jal]
2. **Ring finger** - Earth [Prithvi]
3. **Middle finger** - Space [Akash]
4. **Index finger** - Air [Vayu]
5. **Thumb** - Fire [Agni]

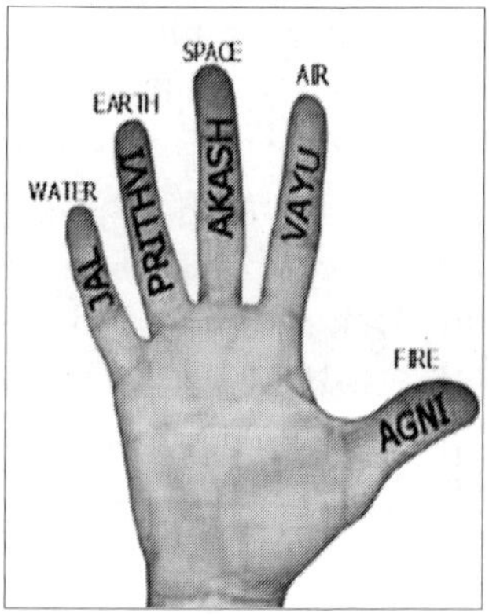

Fig 12.0

The middle finger is the longest of 5 fingers, and it reflects space that is the most substantial part of the Universe as well as in our body. There are billions of cells in our body, and there is an intra-cellular between each of these cells, which makes it the most abundant element in our body.

Mystic of 5 fingers

Mudras are the gestures or indication to lock the energy and steer it back to the body that is released during meditation. It keeps the body in a good health condition and gives discipline and conditioning the focused mind for spiritual pursuit. The Mystic of Mudras offers most convenient, easily operated hands to cure the disease along with prevention. With 5 fingers of your hands, you can miraculously influence the body's metabolic activities, and you can do this while daily activities such as during office time, before sleeping, watching T.V, walking on the floor, etc. The fingers of our hands are considered as divine power.

Significance of Mudras

1. Mudras are a gateway to spirituality.
2. It cleanses the veins, open the heart and mind and improves the immune power.
3. Mudras can be beneficial at the mental and physical level, where the drug fails to do.
4. It can influence the body's gland, control their hormonal activity, and provide health benefits of all kinds.
5. Mudras regulate energy flow, help in enhancing our Aura and improve the functioning of all 7 chakras.
6. It can balance all 5 elements.

Each planet effects on our health.

The connection between the planets describes the health and function of the body. Every living organism is consist of physical elements, both physical and chemical reactions occur. We are the bunch of atoms made of specific elements through the physical bond of the Cosmos, similar to planets are. Built of the same elements, we respond to the cycles of our Cosmos. Our body's chemical or atomic reactions react to the planetary cycles of planets and their proportional gravity. Thus, Planets can affect us, as we all are connected in this universe, we used to live on these rotating planets and breathe, and we constantly exist in a cycle of the Universe. Planets and Stars have a different impact on our life depending on their location or position. The Cosmic forces can control thoughts that can direct our actions. Every planet has its function indicate particular energy and related to health conditions and diseases.

1. **Mercury** - According to Vedic Astrology, Mercury is also known Budh that means wisdom. It shows the degree of excellence, intelligence, and mastership in a person. Mercury is regarded as a planet of logic, and communication. It improves communication capabilities and hand skills. Mercury energy

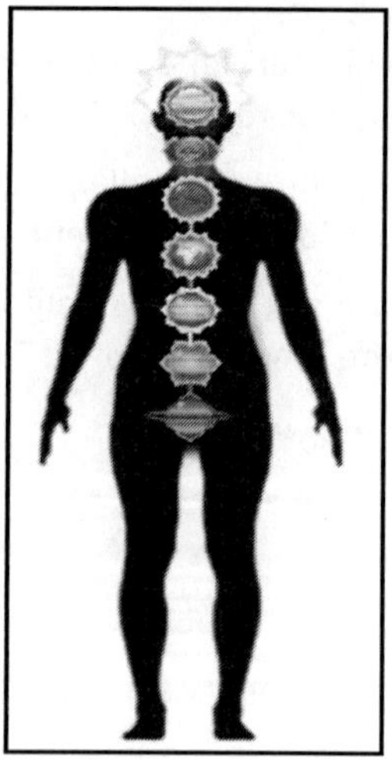

Fig 12.1

governs Body parts like lungs, ear, arms, nervous system, etc. An individual can suffer from weak nerves, scars, wounds, dizziness, excessive hormones, impotence, and backbone issues. It is responsible for giving the problems connected to the lungs and chest.

2. **Venus** - This planet known for romance, love, attraction, sex, music, and amusement sources. Venus assists in the functioning of over nose, eyes, throat, kidneys, reproductive organs, etc. A person can suffer from a lack of romance, attraction, and failure in married life. It can give eyesight disorders, tonsils, diabetes, sexual disorders; Glands problems, blood loss, weak kidneys, and sugar levels issues.
3. **Mars** - Mars is known for confidence, administrative skills, and courage. Mars energy is considered favorable for muscles, Blood, and inflammation. Mars is responsible for muscular pains, scars, wounds, and blood concern issues.
4. **Jupiter** - Jupiter is known for large and vast. Its energy can influence luck, fortune, prosperity, arrogance. Jupiter governs Intestine, fat, and liver. A person may suffer from cold and cough, liver problem, gas, ear problems, and cancer disease.
5. **Saturn** - Saturn is a big planet and is connected with cold and dry. According to Hindu Astrology, being known for Shani means moving slowly. Saturn energy affects the bones, structure, hardening, and skin. Saturn causes blindness, deafness, and paralysis. Other health problems related to this planet are Anemia, respiratory issues, weight loss, and weak joints.
6. **Uranus** - Uranus is a highly significant planet for transforming your personality, bestow creative mind, and having an affirmative attitude toward consciousness and life. The effect of Uranus can influence our nervous system, respiratory functions, lungs, Bronchial tubes, and the diaphragm. Uranus can lead to confusion, diminished intellectual capacity, some loss of sense of reality and memory, bronchitis, asthma, etc.

7. **Neptune** - Neptune considered a planet of spirituality, illusion, nightmares, and fantasies. The health issues it can create addiction, lymphatic system, and real mental disorders. Neptune helps in the function of glands like endocrine glands include the pituitary, thyroid, and adrenals.
8. **Pluto** - Pluto is the slowest and dramatic planet. It can cause an extreme change in tendencies in nature and individual human character. This planet can affect the capabilities of body's to rejuvenate and heal. It regulates various functions of the immune system. Pluto is also known to the regeneration, birth, death, and the body's reproductive system. It can become a reason for severe and crucial illness, accidents and reproductive organ problems.
9. **Sun** - Sun is a powerful, hot and most influential planet. It illuminates our solar system and endows power, prosperity, and dignity. Sun rules over the eyes, brain, skin, and heart. Sun indicates high temperature, eyesight problems, headache, weak memory, heart ailments, dehydration, and excess hunger. Sun's gravitational force can cause tides in the Oceans.
10. **Moon** – Moon is smallest and close to the earth which represents beauty and love. It indicates peace of mind, joy, and enthusiasm in life. Moon can profoundly affect the feelings and emotions of our heart. It controls the fluid of the body like water retention, blood flow, and digestive motion. The gravitational force of Moon can cause tides in the Oceans. The Moon causes stress, depression, mental illness, sleeplessness.

Astrologers follow the development of life sphere through the transit of planets, and its cycles are calculated by mathematical formulas. They combine the functions of planets, aligned with each other, which can describe how they can affect the body. It can show that any health issues can arise.

Overview

Thus, we aware about the substance, whether it turned out to be dark or some peculiar particle. How the cosmic infrastructure is related to human life. According to such an assumption in a concealed or ingenious sight, can be identified with the current technologies, and the forthcoming's potential is practically unending. Everyone has some ability. Otherwise, you cannot live a normal life too. At present, how much we are organized these cosmic forces and all five elements, decide how stable and strong this body is.

By working consciously on these five elements, we learn how to maintain health, and enjoy a long and fulfilling life based on higher awareness. If we cleanse them enough, we can move into mastery of the elements. This body is a play; hence the world is also the universe.

'Planet always helps me to attract happiness.'

Chapter - 13

Frequent eating Meals and Healthy Food Habits

Eating well is a unique art. It will approach you to control the way you eat. There are no calorie counters for measuring or inspection to control whatever goes into your body. You are eating food at the right time, and if you develop a habit of intake of small amounts of food in your body, it will accelerate your metabolism and faster your digestion process. A small amount of meals in three hours and five meals each day. Include this routine in your habit and see its results. Eating well helps your body to burns fat, eat less calories and even prevent you from happening of starvation mode. Eat frequently in a little quantity that will not make you hungry again for the next few hours. The interesting thing about eating after a few hours is that, it makes you feel that as you are eating more food than earlier.

A Singer like Jennifer Lopez usually eats four to five small meals a day. Favorite's diet includes protein shakes, veggie burgers, etc. Salma Hayek intake five small meals a day keeps her energy levels up.

The researcher found that we should not wait for three large meals a day, and it is better to fit in at least five small meals. Thus, on a diet of low-calorie, there is less chance of weight gain, it's always correct to choose split calories food of five or six meals. Eating more often in low-calorie meals helps to burn fat, there are several benefits of it:

(i) **Elevates Mood** - There is a strong link between the mood and food. The brain chemistry can change by eating well frequently. You can include vitamins, protein, carbohydrates in your diet like Fiber, Vegetable, Fruits, Cereals, etc. sustain serotonin levels in the brain. Anti-depressants drug functions likely through increasing serotonin level. The right eating foods can execute the same.

(ii) **Maintain a level of Cholesterol** - The several mini meals maintain a level of cholesterol, and it reduces the cholesterol nearly by eight percent and low-density lipoprotein 'bad' cholesterol levels by twelve percent. More often meals keep blood sugar levels in control, assisting in removing insulin spikes which can affect the production of cholesterol.

(iii) **Maintain Energy** - After digestion, food generate energy for the body, and further body burns this calories and energy for doing work. This process will be disturbed if we skip our regular meals and wait too long without food. If your blood glucose level is high, then you feel more energy and vice versa.

Eating well maintain levels of blood sugar, which means that you will feel more energetic throughout the day. Even researches show that athletes who frequently eat every three hours can run fast and practice for long periods of time.

(iv) **Increase metabolism rate** - Our body is programmed to save energy when the intake of food stops. Blood sugar level usually changes after a few hours, and if we do not eat anything, it increases your blood sugar level. Although, you're metabolic rate may be slow. Eat more often in mini-meals will increase your resting energy and you will burn more calories and reduce the body fat percentage.

(v) **Reduce Weight - It seems Impossible to lose weight when the metabolic rate slows down.** In this way, our body tries to stick to every calorie. Secondly, if we wait for a long time in the middle of the meal, it can cause to bad food alternatives and outcome, there will be no weight loss. Low blood sugar provokes hunger; you will strike down feeling of cravings.

Cravings happen because you leave yourself hungry or usually wait for long hours to eat. But, if we eat often, you could not be gluttonous, and you can make choices and enjoy the best nutritious food. It will be best for you to avoid eating more calories in one meal.

'I enjoy frequent eating small meals diet.'

Chapter - 14

Healthy Eating Habits for Your Child

Nowadays, there are a lot of discussions to fit the kids. Those who can take care of your child are doctors, teachers, parents, and others who have a better experience with kids be fit. Parents provide an atmosphere that helps children's to maintain the lifestyle that is conducive to their wellness. Guiding parents about children healthy eating habits, and casting these etiquettes can assist kids to maintain proper health. Even, if your children are young, eating habits will help them maintain a healthy lifestyle during adults. A parent must have a positive attitude towards the health of their children, and they should assist children's to keep a positive body image. They should set reasonable limits on viewing on-screen entertainment sources such as Cinema, television, mobile, and video games. To promote healthy eating habits include:

Low diet Plan

Many forms of healthy eating, cut your fat, which your child eats. If your child needs a diet change like weight loss or weight gain, you can select any child's health care advisor or specialist who can check the child's growth and weight. Your kids need to follow low-fat diets plan according to their calories need:

- Green vegetables and fruits,
- Dietary Fiber food and best cereals like cornflakes, cracked wheat, barley, maize.
- Reduce the sugar and salt amount in the diet.

Promote kids to eat slowly

Children should adopt slow eating behavior. Before feeding the next meal, children should really be hungry. Apart from this, you never ask for the next meal, as if they look hungry, they will automatically ask for it. You do not need to follow your child repeatedly to eat food.

Make available healthful choices of food in the house instead of unhealthy snacks

Make a wide variety of healthy foods (high in nutrition value) available in the house. It will help your kid to learn about nutrition fact, keep an eye out for high calories and overall fat dietary choices. Leave the useless and unhealthy choices such as soda, chips, and sweetened drinks.

Entire family will take part in fun physical activities

The kids and whole family shall take part in fun physical activities like Jumping Jacks, Balance Beam, Balloon Up, Follow the leader, Hopscotch, Crabwalk. This is one of the best ways to keep your body fit and enjoy pleasure with movements.

Eat all together as a family and ensure a calm and interactive atmosphere

The best way to ensure a relaxed and interactive atmosphere environment on regular meals. Try to enjoy pleasant conversation and sharing at mealtimes. The children quickly leave the table, if mealtimes are unpleasant. Do not waste time in scolding or arguing. Otherwise, kids may learn to associate eating with stress.

Stop eating foods while watching television

Try to avoid eating food in front of the TV; it is possible that it doesn't pay attention to the feelings of fullness. Further, it may tend to overeat. Select your home areas like the dining room.

Do not use food as a source of punishment or reward for Kids

In order to deprive the children of food as a punishment, there is a sense of insecurity in the minds of the children. As kids sleep without dinner, they can keep in mind that they will be hungry all night. Furthermore, whenever we offer sweets or dessert like ice-cream, chocolate, toffies, used for a reward, children can begin to think that these meals are more valuable than other food items.

Your kid's food should be balanced outside the home

Try to search more about the dining at restaurants or try to include a nutrition diet well to pack lunch.

Balanced Diet Chart

Few things parents can take care about serving healthy meals. Teach or guide the children's like that they can take charge too when it comes to wellness. If you are children's, who wants to be fit, here some rules and disciplines to live and follow a balanced diet chart plan:

Up to 3 years - Duration of maximum growth of the baby

Usually, the newborn baby doubles his birth weight by five months of age and three times since the age of 1 year. Two third of brain development occurs during the first year of life. It indicates the significance of proper nutrition for your baby during the initial three years of life.

Baby Diet plan according to Age

Age: 3 - 6 Months: Breastfeeding only

- The baby depends on breastfeeding; it is important for babies as it offers a wide range of nutrition like fats, proteins, vitamins, and antibodies for the baby.
- Include all necessary fatty acids which are required for the proper growth of eyes, brain, and blood vessels.

- Iron in the breast milk is absorbed. It controls anemia in infancy.
- Contains anti-allergic properties unlike cow's or buffalo's milk.

Age: 6 - 12 Months: Breastfeeding + Serve homemade Foods if baby starts eating

- If the baby first starts eating food the first time; it requires your attention, care, and support.
- Keep in mind that your baby will eat gradually. Just one food will be offered at one time. First, the baby could push meal out of the mouth as it does not know the skill to swallow it. Do not force the baby to feed, if it dislikes a specific food.
- Give your baby food in a different bowl. Supplementary food from the market can be appropriate though they are not as nutritious as foods made from home. Thus it is advised not to give family foods in mashed or pureed form.
- Show Love, interest, play, talk while feeding your child. Promote all family members to sit together with the baby. If you feel any illness in the baby after a particular meal, it better to avoid it can cause allergies due to that food.

Be careful about

- Encourage that food you serve looks interesting. Chapatti of various shapes always appeals to children; we should offer meals to a child who is different in colors and sizes. It's better to choose a funny and exciting name like 'Green Chapatti' for 'Palak Roti' and 'Pink Curd' For 'Strawberry Curd.' You can associate dishes with a funny name like "Milk Lassi" can be contemplated with 'Icy castle.'
- Offer a variety of food to a child. If the children do not like milk, try to offer supplements such as clabber, paneer, and yogurt.
- Always offer child-size food and encourage the nutritional value of the meal.

- If child unlike the green vegetable like spinach, Ridge Gourd (Tori / Thurai), Chenopodium album (Bathua), etc. Then offer them with their favorite snacks such as Cutlets, Parathas (Chapatti), etc. Try to connect nutritious foods with their favorite Cartoon Characters.
- Encourage self-eating from a young age. Do not forget to add vegetables to Pasta Sauce and mix soybeans with multigrain flour roti's.
- There is a link between hypertension, raised blood pressure, and cardiovascular problems. Constant consumption of high salt in the diet can increase blood pressure in children and adults which can result in hypertension and other cardiac-related issues. Even this can cause chronic diseases which can be easily safeguarded by taking a simple health step to avoid using more than 5 grams of salt a day.

Tiffin Meal Alternatives - Must be Healthy and tasty.

☞ **Monday -** Vegetable Sandwiches and Chana Chaat.

☞ **Tuesday** - Chapatti with green leafy vegetable.

☞ **Wednesday** - Sprouts and one banana.

☞ **Thursday** - Wheat cookies and vegetable salads, incorporating with strawberry, black bean, Corn, etc.

☞ **Friday** - Cucumber paneer sandwiches and Onion Poha.

☞ **Saturday** – Spinach Rava Idli with Coconut Chutney.

Essential Foods for your child's Immunity

- Ginger, Garlic, and Pumpkin
- Pomegranate, Root vegetables, Citrus fruits
- Curd, Nuts, Seeds, and Berries

Adolescent Health

A Real Truth about Teens

It seems as if it only clarifies the fact that any real pain is seen which I feel every day. I took a subtle look in adolescence, chased it around, talked with him for a while and came in contact with more adolescents and what I found...

Teenagers are passionate and sentimental. Generally, youngsters waste their time in front of their mirror. They always worried about how their appearance. They prefer to talk to their girlfriends instead of relatives and neighbors. Teens engaging in playing sport and outdoor adventures is nothing new. Teenage reputation is to be wild. And, like most conservatives, they believe that in that image there is truth in the western lifestyle. It is surprising that they are not visible on their endless selfies. Eating habits of a teenager are bad, irregular and unmonitored. Girls are forced into an informal form (to be famous), and the boys fill themselves with fatty, unhealthy, high-calorie junk food.

The common issue with a teenager is Depression due to the negligence of the school's work, teacher's complaints and future career, too many expectations, non-acceptance, and image creation. As a result, difficulties can be faced in relationships, and the enjoyment of life can be reduced. In the worst case scenario, it can be the results of suicide.

There are some signs of disease among adolescents with depression

- The sense of hopelessness and Incapability to concentrate;
- Withdrawal from family and friends; and loss of interest in things;
- Feeling of concavity, Crying or Sad mood;
- Sleepless nights, or sleeping too much;
- Appetite Issues from Anxiety - Eating less or eating more;
- Feeling of frustration, Irritability, and tiredness;
- Pain that does not go quickly.

Negative thoughts are the main reason for depression. This is the primary cause which creates depression, and there are different reasons for this in adolescence.

- **Family issues -** Unluckily, some teenagers have to face impractical situations like poverty, misbehavior, domestic violence, and abuse, or any other issues can lead to misery, anxiety, and depression in adolescence.
- **Painful Life event** - like the loss of a loved one, car accidents, Road rage, divorce, embarrassment and harassment due to major incidents. These incidents may lead to sufferings, sorrow, trauma, or can cause depression.
- **Girls are depressed** - There is a high level of depression among teenage girls. They are worried about their body image and social life. They usually compare their lifestyle with the glamorous life of celebrities.
- **Biological/Inherited** - Depression has a biological component and genetic factor. It can transfer from the parents to their children and contribute to the risk of developing illnesses.

Ways to assist Teenagers

The health of adolescence is growing at a high-risk side, and it is no surprise that this generation is now a victim of every health issues mentioned in the book. The problems are increasing, and all the parents are even more worried about your child now. 'Wonders of miracles, they all live.' Do not risk the life of your adolescence. Although, adolescent physiological changes also influence the brain and the nervous system.

To promote good habits and hobbies, start the revivification.

- When your child is young, start scheduling routine around nutritional food and good sleep hygiene.

- Join those activities along with them they enjoy and show that you support them. You can also nurture a positive outcome quickly, like playing games, physical exercise, or writing a journal.
- Being among them, show respect, love, and concerns about your adolescents. Become a positive role model and show them how you respect, whether you agree with it or not. Continuously shouting at a child can harm their feeling and they can feel insecure. Respect their thoughts and encouragement for rational behavior.
- Set the boundaries and limits of your child and help them, so that they can follow the agreed rules. Do not let them break the rules. For instance, push them to complete their school homework, otherwise, do not give them any freedom to enjoy additional activities.
- Sometimes, Physical and Psychological changes in the young body needed specialist help. Even if there is a medical reason for your child's behavior, your physician may be able to discuss the situation with your teen, find out a cause the behavior, recommend a prescribed medication.
- You can stock the house with healthy foods and plan physical activities for the family.
- Eventually, don't neglect the signs of depression. It is treatable, and you and your child have to take responsibility for it.

Help them to Increase their attention towards Exercising

Adolescents should pay attention to the regular exercising, so to achieve what they believe to be the perfect body and they are well equipped for any situation.

Body image creation is the opinion of a person or feelings about the body and physical appearance. By holding the positive image of a body, it indicates that the way your child looks, it feels a sense of satisfaction, appreciates its abilities, and ready to accept its incompleteness or any imperfections.

Nowadays some teens generally too busy due to their idleness. Idleness or Laziness is usually due to lack of self-discipline in life. They don't want to involve themselves in the sports activities, dance, or any other playing activities; they are tending to spend much time seated. They have no time for exercise.

Although, there is nothing wrong in getting involved in daily activities such as you taking a hot or cold shower, going to school, after that you are playing video games with friends, watching television or spending your time in the theater, or listening music. Although, these activities cannot help you in increasing your stamina, or keep you fit or boost your physical health. However, it can increase the risk of obesity, diabetes, hypertension issues which have increased dramatically among adolescents. You can do one thing for your young child that you have to figure out which activity your children want most. Perhaps your child does not like cricket, football or swimming like others. Maybe your child likes to dance, volleyball, tennis or badminton. Regularly ask your children what activity they want to enjoy. Encourage your child to discover alternate ways to be active every day. You can promote your children's to prepare a list of fun activities, which they can prefer when it's time to stop watching TV or playing mobile games.

Speaking of parents, always help a bigger one, if you want your child to be fit and healthy.

How to help the child recover from the trauma

You can take help of a *pediatrician*, and any other counselors may be more effective to recover your child from trauma and to feel safe after a tragedy.

To restore the autonomic nervous system, step by step treatment plan can help to transform the fear in mind into resilience. To treat unresolved traumas or past chronic mental illness, it is designed to be used in a compassionate and empathetic way, which aid in achieving and maintaining both psychological and physical health.

- To help a child experiencing a painful incident. First of all, parents need to be calm and need to start this process you have to connect yourself with your mildness and consciousness.

- Make sure your child that you will stay with him and he is safe now. Use words that show the affections, ability to understand and feel connected to you. Let the child trust you that you can help him.
- You can guide him in simple exercises that can help him to keep safe, calm, and stay in control again. Try to do these exercises with him and that you can check time to time how they are doing.
- Your sound must be soft and slow. Try to figure out that which incident is hurting him repeatedly, listen carefully to his story and make sure that child is comfortable and nothing had happened with him. Generally, children are sensitive, and they tune themselves to what mind and body are telling them. Be careful about and notice every change in their bodies such as sudden change in eyes, the tone of voice, posture, or tears. As soon as you feel that he is out of control, then tell him to stop the story.
- When your child feels relaxed, then try to find out the root cause behind the painful incident and sometimes accidents are due to fire and fast driving, may be caused by harassment that is always painful for the child, and it's not easy to get out of mind. The next you have to associate his mind with positive things. Better to guide child's don't become part of thoughts as they are visitors, they used to go and used to come. Become a witness of thoughts. When you feel, they are trusting you invite them to sense real happiness and continue to notice their all body's sensations and tell them to lift one leg and let it drop slowly-slowly. The essential thing is to teach them to feel happy in any activity they usually do. It encourages neural activity to cure.
- In order to finally release the tension, with a deep breath, ask your child to shout in open place and tell him to fight with his fear and imagine that he had achieved success and eventually got rid of it. Since this process finally provides

your child with more calm and relaxation. You can see it on its face that enables the nervous system to recover it naturally.

- If your child does not know what to do next, suggest him to rest and see more comedy shows instead of watching boring daily soaps and further don't allow him to talk more about the traumatic event.

Your child can experience any health issues. Many problems can be severe, some of them are not so serious. You can get all the information you need about health problems and pay attention to their habits and set limits on unhealthy foods which cause obesity.

Being fit means, your child eats well, regularly do a lot of physical exercises. If you are children's are fit, then their body works well, they feel good, and can perform all the things they want to do.

'I love to see smiling face of
every child in this world.'

Chapter - 15

Significance of Eating Together

Today, enjoying a meal together with family is more important in our lives as life is too busy, because of the more competitive distortions, any options of outside activities, and constant attack of information from modern technological changes. Due to our job or profession or business, you have to work in the community together with all types of people.

In this busy world, children want regular time with parents to discuss the family's perceptions of ideas about his life and society. Even children's are learning about the life and the world from several informants without the guidance, input or filter of parents. After reaching home, everyone is interested in doing their work in the rooms. To talk to each other, maybe one day's only chance is at the dinner table.

I remember the days of my childhood. When I was growing up, every day I always kept looking at the wall clock while waiting for my father so that when I will meet my father, I will start demanding sweets, toys, etc. My mother is a housewife. My brother and I were in the same school. However, my father usually came home after 8:00 p.m. Every day, we used to meet with Dad at 8:40 p.m for dinner. We altogether used to sit for more than half an hour. We usually discuss how our day had gone, talk about worried issues of society and matters which concerned us. Our dinner was our only chance to gather our small family and reconnect with each other again. It was like a reward for the hard work of the day that was a delightful time of the dinner with family. We used to choose different meals for each family member according to different tastes. As a child, I used to be more attracted to sweet dishes and south Indian food.

Now the recent generations believe that they do not have time to cook, especially they like fast food, snacks, etc. because they are working very far from their home. Although, in place of healthy food items, they choose quick meals for breakfast. Daily lunch is available at their workplace. Even they have no option to have breakfast or dinner with family members.

Benefits of eating food with family

Our smart mobile phones and other devices create more distance from our family members; this is a family meal that brings us closer to our family. The experience relationship and mutual love develop over time with the family. When we eat together with the family, we get some benefits –

It helps in developing closer relationships within the family

Eating together plays a significant role in our life and relationship. As the life of the city is so busy, every member of the family lives on various tracks of life. By spending time together over meals, we can stay in touch with each other on a regular basis. You do not have to watch Television, and your mobile should not be used while eating meals with family. You will focus hundred percent on your family members and your meal. This is the best way to connect with a family member by a regular family dinner.

Diet together teaches food stability to children

Parents can easily plan the development of children's food preferences. They can focus on current conditions of dietary supplements, and they can promote patterns of food intake like fresh fruits and beverages (milk, pure juice) in the stocks that contribute to good eating practices. When parents are sitting with children, one of the common threads of table conversation is acknowledged recent changes in our eating environments and physical activity which contribute to healthy eating etiquettes. By growing and raising more of our healthy eating pattern lead to food stability in the subsequent life of young children.

We all plan healthy food together, which is tasty, healthy and less expensive

All the parents, including me, plans for nutrition and choose the finest options available for the vegetables and fruits available at the markets in best prices. My mother used to cook from scratch that is more pure, healthy, and tasty. In the summer, from my childhood days, my father used to bring export quality mangoes boxes for me. He still likes to buy fresh fruits and vegetables from the weekly market at the best prices. On Sundays, we all enjoy fried food because once or twice a week if we intake non-healthy food, then it will not be too much harm to your body. The body easily tolerates if you enjoy the food in little quantity.

Learning about family culture, skills of dining, and social conversation

Eating a daily meal on the table with family members is an excellent opportunity to celebrate with the family. It helps in learning about family culture food, and value of society. Even you are assisted in practicing the skills of dining and social conversation.

Improving health by collecting everyone in the table

Eating together daily meals is very supportive, and it is essential for nourishment and comfort. We know what the source of our food is and we can enjoy freshness and nutrition together with our family, it is the key to improving our health. If we decide to gather everyone to the table and assure everyone to spend quality meal time together, then food is better eaten with the people we love.

'I am always happy to eat together with my family."

Chapter - 16

Nutrition's and healthy eating habits

Life itself is an illusion. Everything is magic in life. If you see milk, it does not appear like you. If you drink milk, then it becomes you. It sounds like magic. What you eat, you are. Only a few diseases have been cured, which is not a miracle. Once you can perform miracles, you are able to cure the disease very quickly. You know the suffering. You are solely responsible for damages, that should be fixed by you only, then it is possible to set all these things because you are making the entire body inside.

God bless us this life to stay healthy till the last moment of life. Due to bad eating habits, the body gets sick. It is better to find the root cause behind the illness. Almost eighty-five percent of diseases can be easily cured through healthy habits. The entire world pretends to follow wellness sobriety of any kind such as fat-free, high protein, or sugar-free.

Understand the real truth, and the mystery of health is 'Nutrition' which can eliminate the term 'Illness' from our life. Join the march towards physical fitness - exercise regularly and find nutritional food sources.

Nutrition and Natural food - Vegetable and Fruits

Today, a large majority of people adopting raw food like fruit and vegetable in their regular diet. Not all enzymes required for digestion are available in the body. The cooking process destroys an essential part in the food of these enzymes. It will never give the

Fig 16.0

same amount of energy after the destruction. With the initiative of eating vegetables and fruits, it helps to reduce your family's risk of many diseases.

Every step towards encouraging diet balance and regular exercising matters in weight loss and overall health. No magic pills are involved in a balance of diet and weight management. Everyone can help their family by selecting more vegetable and fruits in their daily meal.

- Vegetable and Fruits are low in calories. It serves fiber which is essential for our intestines and digestive system.
- Fruits and vegetable are available in an almost limitless in variety. Every time you can try a new meal.
- Fruits and vegetables are quickly available everywhere in the markets. Fruits are nature's treat; you can eat easily eat in raw form.
- Everyone like to eat fruits and veggies, it is juicy, nutritious, and tasty. It is essential for your beautiful skin and prevents even from aging.
- Vegetable and Fruits are rich in vitamins. It makes you more active and energized.

- Eating fruits give appeal to your plate and reduce the risk of diseases like Diabetes, blood pressure, heart disease, and Cancers.

Consumption of most natural foods - Clean food with raw food diet

My journey started in the direction of eating a raw food diet in April 2010. I do not know that it was the right time to start. My thinking changed utterly; I was ready to do some essential things to return to a healthy weight. What will happen if I stop eating human food myself and back to nature with eating natural diet?

Fig 16.1

There are plenty of delicious natural foods like fruits, vegetables, dry fruits that we can enjoy, if we are not using any dressing, butter, or fry them; otherwise, it's hard to fit into your meals. Many ideas were going on in my mind to assist me in preparing a clear meal diet plan.

☞ I always avoid to using the alarm. I wake up between 6:30 a.m. - 7:30 a.m. I start with jogging every morning, usually at 7:30 a.m. After this, I drink juice which is a mixture of vegetables such as Marjosa (Neem), Emblic (Amla), Carrot, Bitter guards (karela), Aloe Vera, Ginger, etc. This is juice is a hundred percent natural and bitter. It ensures the supply of nutrients and fibers in our body. I like to add milk products in daily breakfast which contains full of calcium, protein, and carbohydrates. Milk and dairy products are a perfect source of energy and are full of protein, mineral, and calcium. Even, I like to enjoy every day different kind of milk products like cheese, homemade butter, milk lassi, a glass of milk (skim milk contain only 0.2 fat per 100 ml) without adding sugar, a cup of yogurt, condensed milk, custard, etc. I think children and teens must be encouraged to consume egg and milk products as in this period they are developing their bone structure and muscles. Goat milk is preferable. I often love to eat Barley Rava Idly and Vegetable Rava Upma that is healthy and delicious. Sometimes, I prefer Chaas with cornflakes.

☞ I start my next meal of the day with fruits and vegetable. Every day I eat fruit in the afternoon time. It is better to think of a combination of two or three fruits at one go. I mostly like Mangoes, Oranges, Grapes, Apples, or a handful of Berries, Pear, Apricot, pink guava. I continue to follow this pattern of eating fruits and veggies at lunch and dinner. In lunch time, I choose Leeches, Watermelon, Sweet lime, Banana, Strawberry, Pomegranate, Melon, Soursop, and Pineapple are all excellent choices. However, I need more energy; I prefer to eat sandwiches, sweet potato, carambola, coconuts, etc. I eat salads of tomatoes, cucumber, onion, cabbage, peas at supper (evening meal time). My mother usually cuts veggies such as carrots, tomatoes, parsley, peppers, celery, and ginger for salad. Again, for a healthy dinner, I try to combine a mixture of Nuts like Wall-nut, Pista, Cashew, and Almonds along with Grains like Chana dal or Corn chat, Pop Corn, Mushroom, etc. Take nuts one ounce every day which is fits of your hand. It averagely 27 to 30 individual nuts. It includes fatty acids and protein. They are the best source of nutrients, healthy fats, protein, fiber, potassium, and calcium in our diet.

Fig 16.1

☞ Our body wants to taste a different variety of food; I try to find something different every week. In this way, I get a chance to choose my new favorite fruits, dry fruits or recipes each week. In idle time, I suggest eating nuts, instead of other unhealthy snacks and junk food like Chowmein, Burger, Samosa, and Fried Momos. I primarily use green tea and plain water, instead of coffee, sweetened drinks, and alcoholic beverages. I like being away from human-made foods. I often eat fast food twice or thrice a week or enjoy hard drinks occasionally which body can easily digest and not harmful too much. Craving for junk food and alcoholic beverages is an indication of food addiction, and these regular bad habits can cause physical harm and lead to serious illness. When I feel really hungry, I eat food. It helps in weight management, reduce bad cholesterol, and it keeps away from the risk of diseases such as anemia, diabetes, heart disease, etc.

Healthy Eating Habits in the right way

Eating healthy habits promotes healthy living and longer lives. It is difficult for many people to change eating habits. Maybe you have particular eating habits for a long time, so you will not realize that they are unhealthy. It has already become part of your life, so you do not want to think more about them.

Check what we are eating

Check your present daily diet. Check whether you are eating more food and eating more calories that is not necessary. Do you have sufficient time to burn all calories? You have to consider the food items that are less fat and easy to digest. Spend your time on regular exercise and yoga; this will help you burn extra calories.

Stay far from fast food and soft drinks

Fast food and Soft drinks cause significant harm to our body. It can be unhygienic and contain high sugar content which may tend to diabetes, obesity, etc. These unhealthy junk food add excessive calories to your diet that you do not need.

Select Green Veggies

Keep on adding green leafy vegetables in your diet, instead of junk foods. They are a rich source of vitamin, fiber iron, calcium, etc. Green veggies are easy to prepare and digest.

Chew food properly

In addition to healthy foods, properly chewing may also help in weight management. One of the simplest ways to digest the food is to chew it completely. Many people mostly eat food quickly which do not prove helpful to chewing their food properly. Just double the dining time, reduce your diet to fifty percent according to your calories need. If we see cow while eating food, its chews the food at least thirty to fifty times. The more you chew your food, the easier it is to digest your stomach, and the more calories will burn while moving jaws.

Set your limits on Screen Time

Set the boundaries on the amount of time spent on watching TV, playing video games, and using a smartphone, tablet, or computer. Do not spend too much time on sitting activities, make sure time spend on for active stuff, like outdoor games Tennis, basketball, swimming and several others.

During eating, focus on your diet

Most of our attention is not to cook food or to eat. We concentrate on texting on mobile phones and watching television. How much we eat, we are not counting. We tend to over-eating. If you pay attention only to your diet, then you will eat only as much as your body requires. Next time, when will you sit down to eat your food, keep away your TV remotes, and mobile phones.

Eat food when you really hungry

Before starting to eat food, ask yourself if you are really hungry or not. Hunger prompts your body when it requires to be nourished. Sometimes, it is not beneficial to follow the rules of diet. You are eating as you are pleased, or not fed up. Do you have any other reason for eating? Let the hunger will tell you when and how much you should eat. Do not follow the time restriction on daily diet routines. Just listen to your body and understand the signs of hunger.

Some examples of true cues are:

- Hunger pangs, and rumbling in your stomach,
- Feeling of weakness and loss of energy,
- A Little headache or focused hassle,
- Irritability due to the continuous feeling of hunger.

Some example of false hunger cues are:

- Cravings,
- Eating wafers and enjoying while watching Television like chips,
- Follow what others are eating,
- Eating as you are bored, sad, idle or angry,
- External cues like social events,
- Eating more due to preferred food choices.

It is beneficial to listen to your real hunger cues so that you can understand when to eat wisely and how much food is sufficient for you. Take careful decisions about eating and paying attention to how you feel. Let trust on your body to tell you when it needs food. A bird travels thousands of miles in search of food. Don't be hurry, if you are really feeling hungry, decide what your body needs. You can make a healthy choice and how much meal you want.

Reduce ages in your meal

You should not eat food through day after a certain age. I think you have ever been noticed that it's difficult to lose weight and it more comfortable to gain weight if anybody crosses the age of thirty-five. It happened due to changes in your hormones, eating habits, activity level, and how fat can be stored in the body, and all factors can play an important role. If you are under 28 years, you can enjoy more meals in a day, which will fit well in your life. If you are over thirty years old, it is best to reduce the intake of food during meals.

Best Calorie Counters / Eat per day

Food provides energy that our body needs to function. The Calorie is a measure of energy. An average person requires to eat nearby 2000 - 2500 calories every day to maintain, and 1500 - 2000 calories to lose one pound of weight per week. It considers on many factors such as Gender, height, age, weight, and metabolic health. You can check out by entering details on several apps available on google play as well. For many days, it is advisable to use the calorie counter, so that we can check how much calories, carbohydrates, protein, fat, vitamins, fiber, and minerals we are eating. It can be an eye-opener and supportive in both situations. Whether you are reducing Calories intake for reducing weight or conversely, when you are looking for weight gain, then you need the necessary calories to enter your body. By cutting calories without eating foods is not a sustainable way to lose weight. It works for several people, they choose to live without food, and in the end, they are hungry all the time. It can slow your metabolic rate and cause weakness in your body. It is advisable to make other permanent changes that help in weight management without feeling hungry. Some changes in your diet can help you to lose weight.

Adding more Protein to your diet

Having more protein in your diet can cut cravings upto fifty percent. It increases your metabolic rate, assist in curb your appetite. It can tend to automatic weight loss. Cheese, soybeans, lentils, asparagus, spinach, and Broccoli contain proteins, which are essential for your body growth and boost the immunity system.

Drink water when your body needs it

We all know about the fact that our body is 70% water. It is essential that the body receives its much-needed daily dose of minerals through the water. Drinking enough water detoxify your body and is also necessary for your glowing skin. We must avoid drinking water, eating food; otherwise, it slows down the digestive process. It is advisable to drink water fifty minutes after or before eating food.

Avoid consuming sugary beverages

If you want to reduce weight with minimal effort, then consider making permanent by ellminating liquid sugar calories from your diet. It is top most fattening Items in your Diet and is associated with increased risk of obesity. It includes sugar-sweetened beverages like milkshakes, sweet tea and coffee, and several other soft drinks that contain sugar.

Lower down regular meal of Fattening and Carbs Intake

The way for sustained weight loss is to avoid foods that are full of high calorie, replace them with foods that fill you with fewer calories like fruits and vegetables. Just plan your meal to eat quality fiber-rich carbohydrate sources. If you stick to this diet, the high-calorie composition of your food becomes less important, your appetite level goes down, and you are eating little calories.

Do regular Exercising

When we eat more calories, then our body needs to burn it. Our body should be proactive enough to consume this high-calorie diet. If you don't like to go to the Gym, then consider swimming, play football or tennis, or join any other sports activities that is important for weight loss and optimal health. Naturally, regular exercising also have other benefits that are beyond weight loss like more energy, feeling better throughout the day, long life, lower risk of illness.

Common rules regarding diet

Eating food is also an art, and it has now become part of traditions and culture. Just like money, must be earned through good deeds and only for livelihood. In this way, do not eat food from those who have earned it from unethical means. For everyone who wants to live a healthy and happy life, there are some universal dietary norms for all humans to follow. Let's try to understand them:

- Offering prayer always, before eating any food. The meal that is worshipped endowed you high strength and vitality;
- Eat only when you actually feel hungry;
- Always admire the food. Feel happy to see or eat food;
- Prevent drinking water while eating food;
- Eat enough food for the needs of the body. It does not lead to overeating; it prevents illness.
- Always sit in a clean place to eat food.
- Everyone should consume food items prepared at home.
- Make changes in your diet as per season.
- It is preferable to avoid eating in the bathroom because the negative energy present there can penetrate our body through food.
- The leftovers meals should not be given to others.
- Always wash your hands before eating food.
- Food that serves to you should always be hot and have an appropriate amount of oil.
- A meal must not have uncomplimentary combinations or mixed items (for example, milk and fruits, cereal and pickle).
- The utensils for the meal must be clean properly.
- Food should be eaten slowly, not rapidly.
- During meals, it is better to avoid unnecessary talk and laughter.

Significance of eating fresh food

You can develop the habits of eating fresh food. It ensures better health status as the nutrition is more in natural and fresh food then as compared to prepared food like sweets, several types of fried food items, etc.

This...

OR

This...

Fig 16.3

This...

OR

This...

Fig 16.4

Please look at the both pictures of fruits (Pic-16.2 and Pic-16.3). The more exciting fact about the two pictures, the first row fruits of both photographs seems to be more fresh and tasty than the other. Fresh fruits or cooked food should be exposed to the external environment for a short time. But it is kept for a long time it gets spoiled because the germs begin to grow and they are bad for health. Some reasons are responsible for spoilage of food such as bacteria, Protozoa, Fungi, humidity, temperature, light, and other chemical reaction. Eating a few days old foods for health from a spiritual perspective is also harmful. The interference of negative energies in the environment and the harmful micro-organisms are developed easily if it exposed to the external atmosphere for a long time. This food can adversely affect your mind and body. Eating fresh food within a short period of preparation is necessary. Fresh food can provide more power to the cells in the body, gain the control of life force. It increases hemoglobin level and resistance strength.

Appropriate diet as per the season

Our atmosphere changes according to different seasons. To face these changes, a person has to make changes in the food too. There are many seasons in India. Summer Monsoon and winter are three main seasons in India.

Diet for the Monsoon/rainy season

In the spring season, it is favorable to stay away from the diet that comprises of sweet, heavy oily meal, and sour or acidic items. The food choices like barley, cooked corn, roasted yellow gram, bitter gourd, carrot, radish, yam, raw turmeric, dried ginger, and pepper are easy to digest.

During this month if you adhere to salt-free diet for a week, it is healthy for us. It helps a lot in purifying blood and protects against skin, heart, liver, and kidney diseases. In this season drink every morning mix vegetable juice, especially including neem flowers before eating anything. It will boost your immunity power. A liquid diet shall be allowed in minimum quantity. In this season Intermittent fasting is best for health.

Diet suitable for the summer

The digestive process supplies energy generated through digestion of food required for the functioning of the body. In the summer season, digestive power decreases. It's preferable to add food containing coriander, cumin, cardamoms, and juicy fruits like Indian gooseberry, pomegranate, are beneficial. You should be far away from eating food, which is cold and warm. Olly and fatty food items should be avoided.

Diet fit for the *winter* season

The meal is digested well during this season. Fatty foods such as ghee, milk, butter, should be eaten. The diet consist of sour, sweet, salty and juicy items are beneficial. It's better to stay away from Bitter, Spicy, and astringent juicy items. Oil and ghee should be used according to the calorie need. If you do not like to eat vegetables more, then make a combination of salads and other cereals like Lemon Zucchini Bread with butter, roasted carrots, and cherry tomatoes, you may enjoy. This is an interesting way to get your snacks veggies with delicious tastes.

How to Gain Weight more

Food is a necessary facet of life, and all living creature on this earth depends on food for energy and nutrition. If you want to gain weight, then it requires to eat more calories than your body burns. The target for 350 - 550 calories every day above the level of maintenance. Consider more intake of protein that creates building blocks of your muscles.

- Eat at least 4-6 meals per day for weight gain.
- Add the required amount of carbohydrate, fat, and protein to your diet. You can add spices, sauces to your food, which makes them easier to eat more.
- Eat the essential protein needed to gain muscle weight rather than only fat.
- You can go to the Gym, practice some weight lifting exercises. It will help you gain muscle mass rather than fat, and improve your strength.
- A regular eight hours of proper sleep helps in weight gain.

You can also see several other factors for weight gain. Some of the examples drinking milk (especially full cream), using weight gainer shakes like banana and caramel apple shake, eat actively at normal speed which aids in digestion.

An individual who is underweight can experience health problems. Many reasons for losing weight are thyroid and eating disorders, Diabetes, Cancer, Infections. It's necessary to eat healthy food and follow the overall healthy lifestyle.

Change your diet plan step by step

There is no need to leave all things together to switch to a healthy diet. You do not have to become perfect in a single day. You do not need to change everything altogether. You have to think about your new healthy diet plan and go ahead by the number of small manageable steps - like adding a vegetable salad and sprouts in your diet in evening time instead of evening snacks like chips, samosa, etc. Next week, you can plan for low diet in the dinner. When your small changes become a habit for you, then you can further continue to replace more healthy choices.

If one diet is suitable for a person, then it may not be appropriate for you, because your body can respond differently to different types of foods, depending on the genetics, health factors, and several other reasons. It will take time to find the right weight loss method for you, and it will require determination, patience, and some experiments with various food items and diet.

Some people respond well to counting calories methods; others give better feedback to keep more freedom in planning their weight loss programs. To set yourself up for success, avoid fried foods and change your mindset to eat more raw and fresh food and include nutrition in the diet which is easy to digest and result in physical and mental health.

Every person who understands health is something that you can invent. This is not your opinion. When the process of life is happening well, it is health. If you grant your life to function altogether, it is healthy.

'I am enjoying the blissful taste of nutrition.'

Chapter - 17

Heath Risk and Medicine system

Everyone on this planet is associated with food, eating habits, external environment.

Health Risk is a possibility that can harm your health. A risk factor of health is an attribute or exposure of a person that increases the possibility of developing a disease or injury. Some examples of the risk factors are overweight, high blood pressure, bad eating habits, alcohol and tobacco consumption, underweight and unsafe water and hygiene. What we can do about health is to use the body adequately which could not harm our health, it has everything to make health for yourself. I would say, if we take responsibility and care about health risks then Eighty-five percent of the illness will disappear on this planet. That means only fifteen percent of the ailments would remain; it can be easily handled.

Type of disease

Diseases can be classified into two categories: infectious diseases and non-infectious diseases.

Like, 85% of the diseases can quickly disappear from the planet and the remaining 15% due to various external effects that are not always in your control.

Infectious diseases

Infectious diseases happen because of an external intrusion.

Diseases that can spread through one person to another person are known as infectious diseases. This can be mainly due to infection of microbes. Anyone can be infected with breathing, drinking, eating or touching in which there is a germ. These germs can be bacteria, virus, fungus, and worms. This type of diseases can spread through several means such as by air, water, food, physical contact from one person to another. Cold, Malaria, Cholera, typhoid, plague, tuberculosis, AIDS are some of the examples. You will have to go to the doctor for treatment.

The disease which spread among several peoples in a community, at the same time is known as epidemic disease. It is common for those people who are unaware of the disease spread through microbes. Most of the infectious diseases are contagious causes due to

- Spreading by contact - skin to skin contact, shaking hands, using clothing and the utensils used by the patient,
- A Dirty way of living,
- mucosa from coughing patient.

Common diseases transmitted by touch or contact or speak are cold and cough, sneezing, leprosy, skin diseases, eye infections, and AIDS.

Soil contact can lead to illnesses such as mycosis, tetanus, and infection.

The microbes may be directly engrafted into the skin, for e.g., Hepatitis B virus by unwashed syringes and needles, rabies virus through dog bites.

Non-infectious diseases

Non-infectious diseases are confined to those who suffer from them. This type of diseases cannot be spread from an infected person to a healthy person and it is restricted to the diseased person is called non-infectious diseases. If I say self-created, then it means that it happened from inside you. The classification of non-infectious diseases with some of the examples.

- Deficiency of essential nutrients in our diet, E.g., Scurvy (Vitamin C), Beri-Beri (vitamin B-1), Goiter (dietary iodine);
- Metabolic disorders such as Diabetes, phenylketonuria, Obesity;
- Genetic - Hemophilia, Thalassemia;
- Allergies – Asthma, Hay fever (allergic rhinitis);
- Degenerative diseases (in old age) – Cataract, Arthritis;
- Even due to thoughts and emotions, physical illness can manifest in many ways. Some of the mental disorders are a Social phobia, Depression, schizophrenia.

Careful remedy to protect from the spread of disease

Although this 85% of the diseases (non-transitive diseases) are created on the planet themselves or mind, they are capable of recovering. Let's check out an ingenious analogy, assume any of your body parts is starts acting funny, it's beating you every day, harassing you and tortures you every day without your permission, and then it would be considered as sickness. Just like this, you are doing with your life. You are not taking your life on a more serious note; you're hurting your body every day, making you suffer and cry. On the other hand, everything around you is designed like this, you can quickly change it, but you don't suppose to change. This body has been programmed to live a healthy life. That's why it will never be against you. Either way, you have failed to keep it happy. Therefore, you have to pay more attention because everything in this body was made from within. In this way, you can fix it from within. But if you're going to the doctor, it will prove worthless in the long run. Medical treatment can only assist you to manage the diseases; it does not allow you to get rid of these diseases permanently. Each day, they will add more chemicals to your body, so every day you will cause more disease inside you. Unless you modify the basic model, health will not be there to happen. Swami Vivekananda told that have faith in yourself - all power is in you - be conscious and bring it out. Say, "I can do everything." Beware! No saying "nay," no negative thoughts! Say, "Yea, Yea." All power is within you.

There are many white blood cells inside our body (between 4,000 and 10,500 white blood cells per microliter of blood). These cells help in fighting infections by attacking against germs like bacteria, viruses, and other microbes that enter into the body. If an army of germs in front of you, then your immune system should be strong enough. By which you can live a healthy life forever. However, when we talk about chronic diseases, the main reason for this is always the energy level. Since we have a physical body, we also have an *energy body (Pranamaya Kosha)*. This layer provides the energy infrastructure from which the physical forms are derived. A strong Pranic body is a sign of the better health of the organism. If your Pranic energy body is troubled by the body due to the environment, you live in, or because of your attitudes, emotions, thoughts or *the meal you eat*, this naturally invites physical disorders. Yoga is one cure for all diseases which ensures that if your body is in full flow of energy and is properly balanced. Yoga is the way to make a path to the manufacturer. There is no need for any medicines; it changes your breathing style which improves your blood circulation and body functions.

We must take some precautions to control the spread of infectious diseases:

- Wearing a face mask to prevent the viruses which cause lung disease. However, this mask does not meet the purpose of boosting immunity. It absorbs airborne water droplets that protects you from the inhalation of the virus particles.
- Cleanliness should be planned that can work for everyone.
- Generate awareness among those who don't know about the disease spread through germs.
- Specific measures should be adopted by governments to prevent or reduce the threat.

- Keeping hands clean is the best way to prevent the spread of bacteria.

Type of medicine system

Ayurvedic medicine

In India, Ayurveda is a form of traditional medicine, and it is also popular in other parts of the world. Ayurveda considered as a complete medical system which takes into account the psychological, physical, ethical, and others wellness of humanity. This conception was in practice from 2 millennium and practitioners of modern medicine have now taken into account the significance of this aspect. Ayurveda holds a significant role in keeping the harmony of the science, nature, and the universe. Since the development of its history, Ayurveda has become a useful drug system in India. In the ideological premise, it was probably very advanced and far ahead of its time. It was one of the first medical methods to advocate a united outlook on health or disease cases. Ayurveda is consist of a different way of treatment, like internal cleansing, herbal remedies, diet, yoga, massage, and several others. It is the least of treatment and more concerned to lifestyle. The prevention of diseases is centered on this system. This holistic method of prevention constitutes it a unique and isolated medical system. This approach focuses on the significance of maintaining a proper lifestyle to create positive health.

Ayurveda is one of the traditional approaches in India. Its roots are in folk medicine. The significant feature of Ayurveda is to develop its conceptual structure depend on the outcome obtained from the use of drugs and therapies. It was the first to provide a philosophical pattern with good influence on therapeutic practice. This empowers it to cultivate into a rational system of drugs very early in its evolution and to get isolated from the religious impact. It emphasized on the value of the evidence of senses and human logic.

Homeopathy

Homeopathy is a system of alternative drugs depend on the principles (of like cures like) first developed by Samuel Hahnemann in 1796. A thesis of homeopathy believes that substances that cause symptoms of illness in healthy people will treat similar symptoms in sick people. Homeopathic remedies based on the healing power of the body in which to treat various diseases, excessive dilute quantities of some natural substances are used.

In this alternative medicine treatment, minute doses of substances are used to invoke the body's self-healing ability.

Acupuncture

Acupuncture is a system of Chinese alternative therapy, in which small needles are inserted into particular points in the body. The principle of acupuncture is rooted in the premise that there are patterns of energy flow through the body that are necessary for health. The disruption of this flow is considered to be responsible for the illness. It fixes the imbalances of the flow at the close points of the skin. This therapy is usually used for pain relief. When people are more concern about the side effects of western medicine, they see acupuncture therapy as an attractive non-drug alternative.

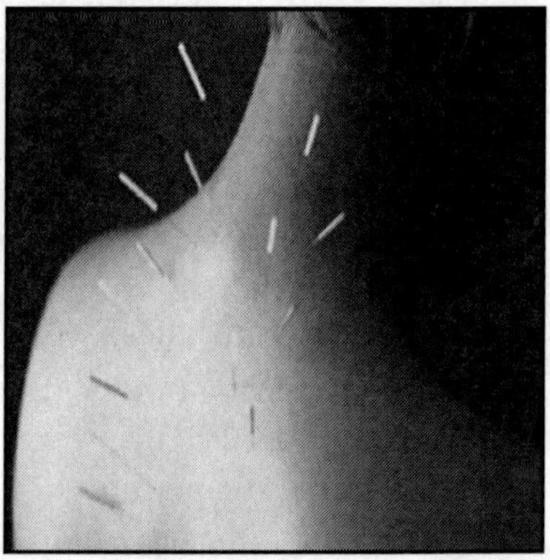

Fig 17.0

In some cases, the advantages of acupuncture are short-lived. You can feel better for two or three days, though this permanent improvement is limited. According to my experience, I would like to suggest to keep massage, Reiki, acupuncture, in the same bucket.

Reiki

Reiki pronounced as 'ray-key' as a spiritual practice developed by Mikao Usui in 1922.

Reiki is a pure and great divine positive energy that finds its source in the Supreme Consciousness. Due to its spiritual background, it has been successfully practiced in the spiritual dimension of life. Reiki is capable of healing anything else that anyone can think.

It can be effectively used for healing of almost everything in the universe, whether it is animals, plants, food, living or non-living things, etc. Reiki is an inherent natural quality, and a wonderful divine gift exists in every person in this world.

Only you have to use your mind, hand, and energies. It is meant to give the reiki energy or vibration to the patient. Energy usually flows between the recipient and the practitioners and both bodies can respond with specific sensations. You have to build your belief system and keep faith in the Reiki treatment, and you're well again with the positive energy of Reiki powers, then health will come. This happened once with me like, I was amazed.

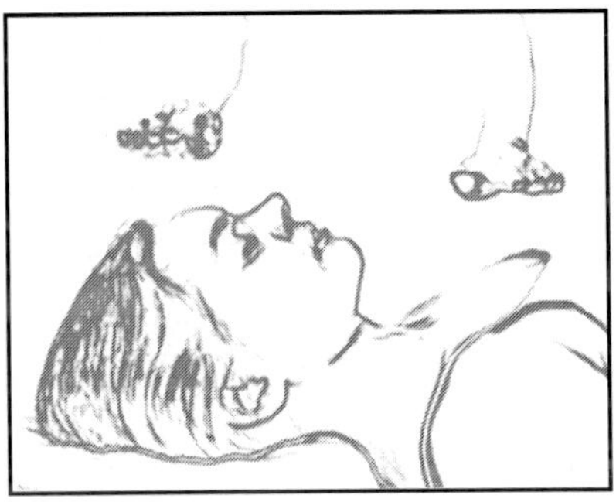

I joined the Reiki Healing foundation ten years ago. Reiki Healing Foundation located in New Delhi was established in 1992 by Dr. N. K. Sharma. This was appealing to me because this institution is showing the right path for every needy person. They used to teach self and other's healing, crystal science, Dowsing, chakra healing, aura cleaning, Past life regression. In the two days class, I had taken a first and second degree of Reiki. This two-level course can be considered for self-improvement and is a pre-requisite for success in life. Even, lecture's on the first day; he guided about daily food habits, deep love for everyone, and good moral and spiritual teachings about being responsible for your behavior. His wife "Dr. Savita Sharma" provided many more practical learning about seven chakras, self, and other's healing. I had learned names, forms, and usage of various reiki symbols on the second day's class. After this, the interesting part of the lectures is subconscious mind training. He provided a live demo of lifting heavy weight person from two fingers which is too much exciting and surprising.

During an introduction talk, he instructed everyone that he usually does not make the followers, he said: "wake up and run away." He wants everyone to be independent in life and start healing for every being in this world. He has a clear perception about God that there is only one power and the name changes only by cultural or religious preferences. I had started the daily healing process of Reiki on different parts of my body. I was under the impression that the energy of Reiki was the same things as the Holy Spirit. I knew that Reiki was real because there was no inclination for Gods involved, I became a kind of reality analyzer. After a month's practice in my bedroom, I had experienced that I became a perfect self-healer, and could provide other treatments too. In this energy soup, all my thoughts about the superstitions are no longer present. It was a wonderful experience with Reiki Healing foundation which I believe that Dr. N. K. Sharma always ethical in the use of supernatural powers.

Home Care and Treatment

Sometimes people choose home remedies for the treatment of body ache, cold and flu, minor injuries, recovering and managing depressions and others. The best home remedies for body pain include drinking water and a lot of fluids and staying hydrated; a person can try the following treatment at home to help reduce the inconvenience:

- Getting Rest allows the body to repair and recuperate. It boosts the immune system fight against the viral infection more effectively.
- Drinking a glass warm water first thing in morning reduce metabolic waste, aids in constipation, burn away toxins and improve blood circulation.

- Hot baths and massages can help relax muscles and reduce stress in the body.
- Antibiotic creams and ointments prevent infection. It can be applled on your burn and cover with a cling film or a sterile, non-alcoholic cloth. Drugs like non-steroidal anti-inflammatory medicines can reduce pain and swelling.
- Placing a cold cloth on the head helps in regulating the temperature, which may include reducing fever.
- Dehydration may result in the rise to temperature and often cause to low blood pressure, headaches, muscle cramps, dizziness. Lots of fluids and placing a cold cloth on the head can help to reduce achiness caused by dehydration. It helps regulate temperature, which may include:
  - Lowering a fever,
  - staying cool or keeping warm to alleviate shivering &
  - Preventing muscles from seizing up.

If you feel home remedies are not ineffective for you, or if the pain in the body becomes more intense then you should consult your family physician or any other doctor.

We sought to understand the perspectives of health risk and several medicine systems. If mind and body are working well, then your energy is supporting to make sure that nothing goes wrong, that is health. Life is happening in full flow; it is health.

I'm glad to know about health risk & medicine system.

Chapter - 18

Symptoms of Body & Amazing Facts about Water

A healthy person never feels that he is healthy, only a sick person interested in health. At that time you will feel health when you come out of your illness, you become healthy. After that it begin to be your natural experience of your routine life, you have no sickness contrast to compare it with. Just like that as soon as you get a headache, you become aware of your head.

However, do you know that before your body gets infected with any disease, your body indicates warning of waning health for a long time?

Our body whispers to us, and if we do not hear whispers, then our body screams.

How do you know that your body is whispering? See below some warning signals.

Diarrhea - This means you have quite loose or liquid stools four or more times in a period of time. It is an ordinary symptom of gastrointestinal distress including bacterial/viral infections; even it is a sign of anxiety and bad eating habits. It causes due to food poisoning, indigestion, etc. You should immediately consult to nearest doctor for its treatment.

Fever - A person who suffers from fever, has a body temperature above the average temperature of 98.5 degrees Fahrenheit. Some symptoms connected with fevers include a headache, cold, shivering, clammy skin, and an inability to concentrate. The fever is caused due to infection of microbes. You can try medicines like Crocin after asking the doctor, or you can visit any physician if it is above the temperature of 101 F.

Stomach ache – Stomach ache shows there is pain occurs between the chest and the pelvic region. It causes due to constipation, indigestion, etc. The symptoms relate to stomach pain include Gas, Indigestion, bloating, chest and pelvic discomfort. It often caused by a poor diet, acid reflux, distention of an organ. Home remedies are adequate if the pain is not too severe.

Cough – A Cough is the rapid eviction of air from the lungs when the vocal chords are open that gives a cough its predictable sound. It can be productive or dry, that means they clear the lungs of phlegm and mucus, and are often a symptom of a respiratory infection or environmental pollution. The common causes are Asthma, Smoking, Viruses, Bacterial infection, and other several factors like damage to vocal cords, postnasal drip, etc. The standard treatments for coughing include rest, humidification, fluids, and over-the-counter medication.

Body Pains - Pain in muscles, bones, and tissues often feels uncomfortable in the form of symptoms of flu, cold or hard work. Many people suffer from body pain due to depression or emotional distress. Body pain gets better with rest and massage. It rarely requires medical treatment.

Headache - These are frequent pain and stress in the head. Tension and migraine headache are common types of problem due to lack of sleep, swelling in the brain, gas, indigestion, etc. Pain medication, rest, meditation helpful in relieving headache.

Rash - A skin rash is a noticeable change in color of skin or surface of the body that has become swollen, red, bumpy, itchy or irritated. The common cause of skin rashes are fungal infections, allergies, eczema, chickenpox, Psoriasis, sun damage, and others. The severity and type of rash you have will determine the appropriate treatment.

The proper remedy is medications, consult any dermatologist, and take care of some precautions like

- Use warm water instead of tap water,
- Stop changing new cosmetics,
- Medicated dandruff shampoo,
- Ensure proper sanitary conditions around you,
- Use gentle cleanser instead of ordinary soaps,

Fatigue - Fatigue is the feeling of being bone-tired, exhausted, malaise, listless, and wholly depleted of energy. The main causes of fatigued extreme exertion, lack of sleep, medication side effects. Some symptoms are continuously tired, impaired memory, sleep issues, pain in muscles, lack of motivation, sore throat, headache, and several others. The standard treatment for Fatigue is adequate rest, healthy sleep schedule, and over-the-counter medication.

Your bathroom can say about overall health status

It's quite surprising that your bathroom can say about your overall health status. Directly bathroom habits may guide us about

- Absorbing fat properly,
- Have blockage or not,
- Getting enough water and fiber.

If you take a peek at your poop, all the things can be revealed.

How often visit Bathroom

How often do you go to the bathroom depends on person to person, you must go once or twice in a day is ideal. Is your stool soft or hard?

- If It is hard, then you are obviously constipated or dehydrated, you should make changes in the diet such as add more fiber and try to drink more water.

- If it is too soft and liquid, then your food is moving through you very quickly.

So pay more attention to your body. Generally, the faster your metabolism, the more you poop. People with slow metabolism usually go to the bathroom once or twice a day. Adequate sleep, Regular exercise, and few dietary changes will keep your metabolism going at a steady pace.

What you eat in your meal can affect how fast your food moves through your body. Sometimes, something moves through your body rapidly it does not necessarily mean that you were capable of utilizing the energy from that food efficiently. That is what all about a healthy metabolism. Even, many factors that are not directly related to digestion such as your weight, gender, age, exercise routine, health issues, and hormones that can influence your metabolism.

Pay Attention to Your Poop

Occasionally changes in smell, size, color, shape, etc. not usually a big issue and it may be related to what you ate recently. Although, if you see a sudden change which is not able to get away, then you have to go to the doctor.

Smell

Your poop is never going to smell like a flower, but it shouldn't be smell nasty at all. If this happens, then it can be an indication that whatever your body is not absorbing from your diet. Underlying problems could include food allergies, infection, Crohn's disease, irritable bowel disorder, or Celiac disease.

Size and Shape

The bowel movements must be torpedo-shaped and soft, enough to pass smoothly. If they become skinnier over time, it may indicate something serious, such as colon cancer/polyps.

What is in the toilet looks like a bunch of rocks? It was hard to pass; you need more fiber to help it pass through before the water is reabsorbed.

Color

The color brown is good. All other colors can be indicators of some things in the body that require to be addressed. E.g.

- Black means the upper gastrointestinal bleeding can occur,
- White could indicate a pancreatic issue or liver disease,
- Red could denote lower gastrointestinal bleeding.
- Yellow could signalize parasites/gallbladder trouble.
- Green could mean Crohn's Disease (IFD – Inflammation and scarring in the intestine).

Improvement in Bowel Movements

If you require improvement in your bowel movements then try:

- Adding more fiber to your daily meal.
- Drinking as much water as possible and start the day with hot water with lemon.
- Include fresh fruits and veggies in your diet.
- Getting involved in light exercise every day.
- In the morning, do some few yoga poses can be a good move.
- Avoid eating food at night.

Amazing facts about water

Water Mantra

Water is essential to our lives, even a life creator. You cannot imagine being on earth without water. The soil without water and nothing is growing on the surface of the land would be inanimate, dead, collapsed into the sand. Our Scientists believes that water always remains in the same amount on Earth. About 97% of the water on the earth is salted due to the sea and not even suitable for a drink. The next two percent is locked in the form of glaciers above the ocean. The remaining one percent is left only for all humanity needs.

Water regulates the temperature of the earth. When the Earth becomes warm, then water cools the surface of the earth. Even, it controls the human body's temperature. It carries oxygen to the body cells and cushion joints, removes the waste, protects organs, tissues of the body. Almost seventy percent of the human body and the human brain is water. The seventy-five percent of a living tree is also water. The famous cardiologist Dr. Anuj Shrivastav from Mumbai recommends to all human beings, which he has called 'Water Mantra.' It consists of 3 simple things.

- Drink two glass of water at least first thing in the morning.
- Drink a cup of hot water after 40 minutes of each meal.
- Avoid drinking water while standing,

Dr. Shrivastav tells us, "If you follow these three things, very minimally you will have to go to a doctor." About the drinking of two glass of water or one liter of water in the morning, Dr. Shrivastav states, "It doesn't matter even if you don't brush your teeth. By drinking water on empty stomach, the alkalinity of mouth will help to dissolve the alkaline minerals inside the stomach." He recommends pH between 7.5 and 8.5 as the best pH for water because the best absorption of minerals from water in this pH range is inside the body. The kidneys will start extracting toxic substances from the body says Dr. Shrivastav "This will rejuvenate your health," "Forty minutes after every meal drink hot water" is the next recommendation of Dr. Shrivastav. By doing this, "Hot water helps to dissolve the fatty contents inside the intestines."

We should drink water while sitting instead of standing Dr. Shrivastav says, "According to Ayurveda drinking water when standing creates an imbalance of 'vata' (wind humor), and this will cause joint problems."

Experiments with the effects of our thoughts on water

Our Earth is encompassed mostly with beautiful nature. It always creates a beautiful design. Today's modern age man has started to think of nature very ordinary and despised. Although humans are a part of nature, often they understand life as a separate category from natural phenomena.

Masaru Emoto was born in Yokohama, Japan, and got a bachelor's degree from Yokohama Municipal University. In the mid-1990s, he started studying water in more detail. His idea was to freeze water and observe it with a microscope to see something like snow crystals. Two months later, this test was successful, and the hexagonal crystal made from this experiment was seen to be beautifully shining. So, he decided that further in this direction he needs to do more researches.

He said that water was a "blueprint for our reality" and that emotional "energies" and "vibrations" can change the physical structure of water. In their water crystal experiments, consisting of

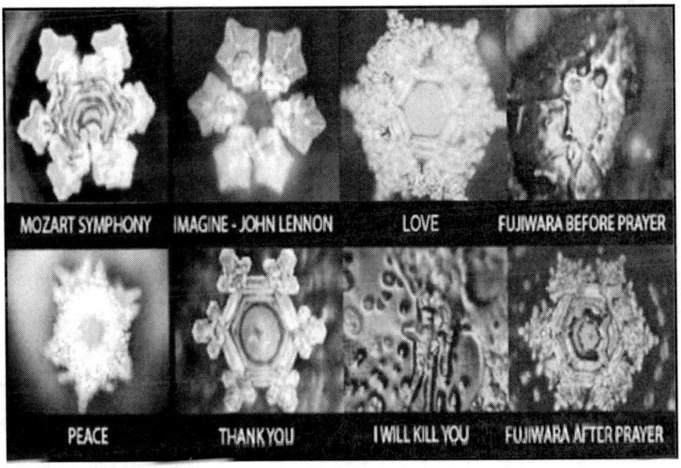

Fig 17.0

exposing water in glasses to different pictures, words, music, and then freezing and examining the aesthetic properties of the resulting crystals with microscopic photography. Emoto claimed that water coming contact with positive speech and thoughts resulted in visually "pleasing" crystals were being formed. However, when that water was frozen with negative intention, it resulted in "ugly" frozen crystal structures. The observation was conducted in different ways. He observes the crystal of frozen water:

- after showing letters to water
- Showing pictures to water
- Playing music to water
- Praying to water

In 2008, he published his results in the Journal of Scientific Exploration; a colleague reviewed scientific journal of the Society for Scientific Exploration. The work was conducted and authored by Masaru Emoto and Takashige Kizu of Emoto's own IHM General Institute, along with Dean Radin and Nancy Lund of the Institute of Noetic Sciences, which is on Stephen Barrett's Quackwatch list of questionable organizations. In the research, more than five hundreds of people focused on feelings of positive thoughts (gratitude) toward water stored in bottles, which was then frozen and its crystalline structures inspected. The gratitude focused crystals were rated slightly more "beautiful" than one set of control crystals and a little less "beautiful" than the other controls. So, the pictures of crystals are neither religion nor science. It is related to nature. Human survives

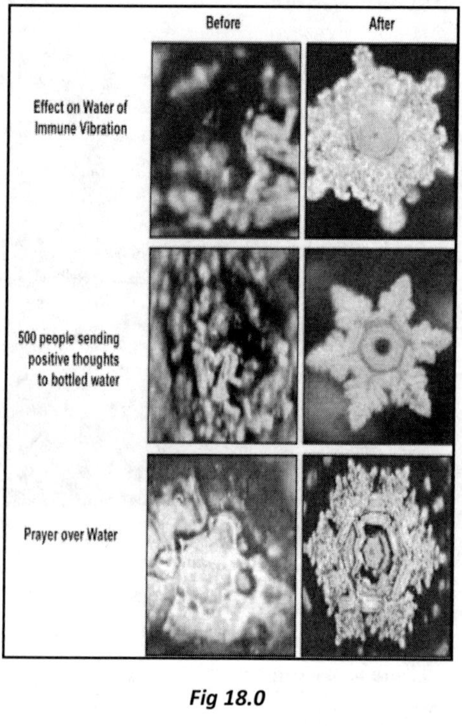

Fig 18.0

with nature. Yet, the world it shows is the truth, and there is no question that many essential things in our lives are still hidden in it.

'I enjoyed learning new type of art.'

Chapter - 19

Change Your Thinking, Change Your Life

I have seen thousands of people in my life; they always prefer to live their life in stress. The reason for this either they do not have any awareness about the same, or sometimes what they developed the habits in their childhood days. It seems impossible to change later in life.

If we try to change the way we think about stress, then there may be a big difference in your life. We want people to identify this challenge that we have encountered in our lives. This challenge is pervasive throughout life. Although, we do not accept it.

Even, I had to face these challenges in my life. With the pressure of CS examinations and due to regular stress on the workplace, I lost all my consciousness. The tension was increased almost twice due to a vehicular accident. The growing interest turned into the uncertainty of my life. It influenced me every part of life, from what time I wake up in the morning, throughout the day what I could afford to do. My nights were also full of restless, and weight was increasing continuously due to chronic stress over long a period. I thought nothing could be done to change the situation or to avoid it. However, sometimes anxiety can teach us a better lesson for your life. It can help us to face the challenges of life. If one door is closed, the other is opened.

After all, I met him at the place where there is no darkness, my life Coach "Mr. Rajender Mahajan." After the first meeting with him,

I have never been surprised by the biological deception of pain and fear. His voices knocked the door like that were seems to cut off the smell of negative thoughts. He helped me in times of crisis, due to his special effort, my depression had disappeared. He never taught me to fight against an external enemy, always against one who is an internal one. By feeding the information regularly can get the people to believe almost anything, which can help to complete dominance over the mind. He told me to absolute control over every action and thoughts of its.

I started focusing on the life fantasy once again and add title C.S as an initial before my name. I was beginning to believe that I'm "C.S Vikas Aggarwal." A Few years later, I felt that I am immensely lucky as managed to clear to my all Company Secretary exams. There is no substitute for hard work and firmness. I noticed mostly students who are appearing for professional courses like Chartered Account and Company Secretary do not have enough confidence. They always comment that "probably will not get success." If you are conservative, then it is unconsciousness. It's nonsense, and it's almost a big waste of time. The aim of life should not be to prevent itself from succeeding; it is by building loyalty that it should be able to control it.

I had the same positive approach in respect my case of a car accident that I always kept myself imagining that "The lawsuit has been resolved in the absence of a witness." Eventually, everything that connects to firmness, the belief power automatically addresses all type of issues. Finally, I won the lawsuit by merely trusting on belief power. His next advice was to learn the Reiki. He said that forget about your sufferings and start the healing of others. Practicing the right techniques to accept it, conquer your fears, and being the best will be beneficial. I joined the Reiki Healing foundation in Delhi. I learned about self and other healings, diet rules, healthy eating habits, and several useful things.

We are fighting with those habits which are deep-rooted. Lack of awareness, a rigid lifestyle, outside pleasures, and over-exposure to a craving for food, though it seems impossible. What is going to happen to a life of human beings? Even our current educations system is not bothered about the truthiness of life. They are still very far from spirituality.

We have to educate school children about the harmful effects of harsh lifestyle and the risks of contracting lifestyle diseases. Moreover, it is important to catch people young, as eating habits are developed in childhood days.

The objective of changing the behavior of children and its education will help present and future generations and save millions of lives.

A Positive attitude is a way for Improved Well-being

Having a sense of self-confidence and positiveness can balance your life. In addition, it makes easier to take healthy food decisions and stay active. It will assist you in

- taking time in solitude, silence during each day provide you strength,
- You will experience the truth of love and acceptance that will acknowledge tolerance and waste in rejecting yourself and judging others;

Be careful with the options for your overall health and well-being. Nothing is more crucial than your care. Set aside time for yourself every day. Some additional tips for staying positive include:

☞ Enhances our attitude of simplicity;

☞ Try to balance both your personal and working life;

☞ In idle time, listen to music or read inspirational books or watch motivational videos on the internet;

☞ Try something new like any activity or hobbies or food and anything that you can enjoy;

- Reduces trust in others; Be more sensible for strength in your life;
- Mind your work and turning inward will overcome your depression;
- Find ways to relieve anxiety, such as yoga, aerobics, other physical activity or relaxation techniques;
- Appraise yourself. Set Long-term and short-term goals of life and provide ratings for yourself;
- Adopt flexibility in your behavior. And return immediately to track;
- Plan mini vacations two or three times a year. Go away from the office or everyday life for a few days in a year;
- Try to spend your time with your friends and family. Ask for assistance whenever you require support from them. Limit your exposure to negative friends;
- Safe inner fire. Identify areas of anger, fear, greed, and others (review day activities and our reaction to them);
- Always keep a positive attitude towards your kids. Become a motivation for your children, how good it is to lead a healthy lifestyle;
- The habit of adequate sleep is one of the best things for yourself.

Things to consider the sources of healthy life

A healthy body is like a crown so that a sick person can see. Whether it is business or any related property, enjoyment, etc., everything is related to fitness. If the body is not healthy, then everything happens but incomplete. Nobody wants to be sick. What are sources of healthy living? We are connected to the world where the aim of diet, sleep, happiness, exercise, a healthy body is to collect concrete evidence about how this proposed intervention will be about good consequences. We need to make immediate changes in our lifestyle like:

- The most significant is an exercise which can be very productive to come in shape. Exercise keeps the mind fit; regular activities gain power, flexibility, and energy from the body. Without regular exercising, the illness comes soon.
- Further, there is no such thing as our food that is making the body sick. What is the food to eat, what is the food to eat or not? We should think about it. Eating right is the best way to effectively maintain or lose weight until you get to your ideal weight. Sustaining to a healthy diet can be tough, considerably in fast-moving modern life. However, in the long run, maintain healthy diet alternatives become naturally rewarding.
- Next, if you do not sleep well, then you can get sick. So you should know how much sleep is required in one day. Usually, an adult need 7 to 8 hours per night seems to best for longevity.
- Happiness is the means of being prominent in life. Without love, peace, and satisfaction, happiness cannot come in our lives forever. Increase your humility by helping yourself to avoid unnecessary ego.

The work of these four sources is like the four wheels of the car. If a wheel becomes rigid, which can be challenging to drive. Our body lives with us in all kind of circumstances, even if it is good or bad. Anyone in this world will be ready to help you in the worst times? If our health is perfect, then we can face any worse situation in our life.

My aim in life is the happiness of human beings. I believe that if you want to maintain good health, then you should exercise physically for 40 minutes daily and use 20 minutes for meditation. Please pause for few seconds before you speak to consider your words.

Fig 19.0

Health does not always come with money and medicine. It comes from peace of mind, balanced food, regular light exercise, fresh air, clean water, adequate sleep, hygiene, routine medical check-up, laughter, and love. It is true that "Health is wealth, it lives in Happiness."

I am happy to change my thinking.

Reference Link

Chapter 1 – Image Links

Fig 1.0 - https://dementiainmyfamily.org.au/age-5-8/the-brain/;
https://es.kisspng.com/kisspng-xf7ygu/preview.html;

Fig 1.1-http://madamelefo.com/child-eating-healthy-food-thumb-1

Fig 1.2 -https://www.dreamstime.com/stock-illustration-boy-angry-standing-road-city-background-cartoon-full-color-image73059736

Fig 1.3 - https://www.colourbox.dkvektorcitron-tegneserie-vektor-5549651; https://www.everymum.ie/my-life/health-well-being/how-do-your-emotions-affect-your-health

Chapter 2 – Image Links

Fig 2.0 - https://www.nihaoindo.com/the-elephant-rope-sebuah-cerita-inspirasi/maxresdefault-6; https://naturalhistory.si.edu/onehundredyears/featured_objects/Fenykovi_elephant.html

Fig 2.1 - https://cgslate.com/blogs/article/myths-and-facts-brain-connections
Hyperlinks of Amazing Facts about Human Brain

https://www.quora.com/What-are-some-interesting-and-fascinating-facts-about-human-brains

Fig 2.2 - https://health.planetfem.com/memory

Chapter 3 – Image Links

Fig 3.0 - http://lordbuddhaworld.blogspot.com/2009/06/sabba-papassa-akaranam-kusalassa_07.html

Fig 3.1 - https://croire.la-croix.com/Abonnes/Formation-biblique/Nouveau-Testament/Saint-Paul-portrait-d-un-entrepreneur-a-part

Chapter 4 – Image Links

Fig 4.0 - https://www.discprofilecanada.com/everything-disc/everything-disc-productive-conflict/workplace-conflict-is-inevitable-2

Fig 4.1-https://in.pinterest.com/pin/534450680751443199/lp=true

Fig 4.2-https://www.team-bhp.com/carpics/MarutiCelerio/I/ Interior%20Front/maruti-celerio -13.jpg

Chapter 11 – Image Links

Fig 11.0 - http://www.innercirclefoundation.in/aura.html

Fig 11.1 - https://dutchsmilingyogi.com/yoga-and-the-seven-chakras

Chapter 12 – Image Links

Fig 12.0 - https://in.pinterest.com/pin/533465518343826599/

Fig 12.1 & Content reference link -http://www.healingenergytools.com/governing-planets-in-the-human-body

Chapter 16 – Image Links

Fig 16.0 - https://universityhealthnews.com/daily/memory/brain-food-what-to-eat-to-protect-your-memory; https://www.smartmeetings.com/meeting-planning/99039/serve-brain-food-next-event

Chapter 17 – Image Links

Fig 17.0 - https://mylocalnews.us/community/business/modern-acupuncture-set-open-first-location-scottsdale

Fig 17.1 - https://floraremedia.com/is-reiki-real-and-is-it-effective/?v=c86ee0d9d7ed

Chapter 18 – Hyperlinks of Amazing facts about water

Content reference link - http://www.masaru-emoto.net/english/ water-crystal.html

Fig 18.0 - https://thekriokcult.files.wordpress.com/2015/02/water-memory.jpg

Fig 18.1 - http://shardy.net/blog/masaru-emoto-water-crystals

Chapter 19 – Image Links

Fig 19.0 - https://9gag.com/gag/a1QeqXw?ref=fbpic&fbclid=IwAR1zFwx5p66j-qKNX9R1wQVDaVLKNgOoKLJMKZ24pMNzyzmdskekDNLTK0c